Cinderella
CANCER

To my wife, Elizabeth,
whose love and support underpins the whole of this story.

© Ray Donnelly 2006

Published by The Bluecoat Press, Liverpool
Book design by March Graphic Design Studio, Liverpool
Printed by Ashford Colour Press

ISBN 1 904438 37 7

Front cover
March 1993. Meeting Roy for the first time at the Albert Dock in Liverpool. Roy had come to Liverpool to launch a street poster campaign for the Lung Cancer Fund.

Acknowledgements
Liverpool Daily Post and Echo for permission to use their photographs.
Back cover photograph by Jim Connolly.

Cinderella
CANCER

A personal history of The Roy Castle Lung Cancer Foundation

Ray Donnelly

The Bluecoat Press

Contents

Professor R.J. Donnelly MB BS FRCSE FECTS

Ray Donnelly was born in Glasgow in 1936, graduated from St Mary's Hospital Medical School in 1961 and became a Fellow of the Royal College of Surgeons of Edinburgh in 1969. He was a research fellow at Harvard University in 1973 and in 1975 was appointed a Consultant in Liverpool specialising in paediatric cardiac and adult thoracic surgery. From 1979 he devoted himself entirely to thoracic surgery, developing a number of innovative techniques and establishing an international reputation.

Author of over 75 scientific papers and a similar number of presentations to learned societies he was elected to membership of the American Association for Thoracic Surgery, the European Association for Cardiothoracic Surgery and the Society of Thoracic Surgeons USA. He served on the National Executive of the Society of Thoracic and Cardiovascular Surgeons of Great Britain and Ireland and was chairman of the Medical Research Council Working Party on cancer of the oesophagus. He has travelled widely as visiting professor to several universities abroad. He retired from surgical practice in 1998 and was appointed Professor of Lung Cancer Studies at Liverpool John Moores University.

In 1990 Ray Donnelly founded the Lung Cancer Fund to raise awareness of the seriousness of the problem of lung cancer and to promote an intensive research programme into the causes, prevention and management of the disease.

In 1993 he conceived and developed the idea of an international centre for lung cancer research to be situated in Liverpool. Roy Castle was approached to give his name to the appeal to build the centre and such was his contribution that, twelve months after Roy died, the Trustees of the Lung Cancer Fund agreed to a proposal from Ray in 1995 to change the name of the charity to the Roy Castle Lung Cancer Foundation.

The speed and extent of development of the Foundation was so great that, in October 1998, Ray stood down as Chairman of the charity after eight years to concentrate all his time and efforts in supervising and developing further the research and other lung cancer initiatives of the Foundation in the unpaid role of Medical Director.

He retired as Medical Director in March 2000, having been appointed Vice President of the charity. He became President of the Foundation in 2001.

Ray Donnelly is a keen golfer and lives with his wife, Elizabeth, at the Albert Dock, Liverpool. They have five grown up children and two grandchildren.

Introduction

My father was diagnosed with lung cancer when he was 70 years old, in 1980. Remarkably he survived the operation to have a lung removed and lived for another 11 years until the disease caught up with him again. In 1992 Professor Donnelly, having read an interview in which I talked about the death of my father, invited me to a reception on the terrace of the House of Commons where he was to raise awareness of the Lung Cancer Fund, a young charity dedicated to the eventual eradication of this pernicious disease. After listening to Ray's address on that day and with my own first hand experience of looking after my father during the last few months of his life, it took very little persuasion for me to accept Ray's invitation to become a patron of the charity.

It has been a privilege for me to have been involved over the years, albeit in a very small way, with what is now known as the Roy Castle Lung Cancer Foundation, and a very particular privilege to have witnessed how Roy's extraordinary energy and dedication in the last year of his life helped build the International Centre for Lung Cancer Research and so turn Professor Donnelly's dream into the ground breaking reality that it is today.

Robert Powell

Chapter 1

'Roy Castle Has died'

The bleep went off in my pocket as I was reading the lesson at the funeral of Ray Wanless who had lost his own battle against lung cancer one week before. It was the signal that Roy Castle had died. I had been warned before going into the church that news of Roy's death was imminent and therefore my bleep was on vibrator mode so that it would not disturb the service. The previous evening I had spoken on the telephone to Roy's wife, Fiona, who was extremely distressed by the breathing difficulties Roy was experiencing as he slipped deeper into coma. I tried to reassure her that it was she, in fact, who was suffering more, since Roy was unconscious. She could only watch and listen helplessly.

The once superbly fit body of one of Britain's best-loved entertainers was making its last brave efforts to resist the devastating course of lung cancer. Before the night was over, Roy had died and both he and Fiona were at peace. Within hours Fiona was to appear on television, composed and full of faith, to thank everyone for their prayers and good wishes and to plead, "No fuss, no tears, just joy".

Newspapers, radio and television were full of the news of Roy's death. It was a national event and many thousands of people all over the country felt a genuine sadness at the loss of someone they had grown to love and admire as he publicly fought and lost the battle against the dreadful disease which he had never deserved to have.

Roy had been a public favourite for many years and generations of young people had grown up watching him on *Record Breakers*. He had a reputation as a multi-talented performer with a hugely attractive and genuine personality, a man of great energy and popular appeal, much loved by his peers and colleagues in the entertainment industry.

But it was the manner of his death and the way in which he conducted himself during the two years of his illness that really captured the heart of the nation and ensured that his memory would burn bright long after he died.

But how had this come about? How did he come to be identified with lung cancer, passive smoking and a charity which later came to bear his name?

Chapter 2

Cinderella Cancer –
An Abominable Disease

Roy was diagnosed with lung cancer early in 1992. Two years before this, when Roy was blissfully unaware of the tragic events which lay ahead of him, but when in all probability the cancer was first beginning to assert itself in the cells of his right lung, I was sitting in my office two hundred miles away in Liverpool with my secretary and one of my patients outlining my plans for a lung cancer charity.

I had come to Liverpool in 1975 as a consultant cardiothoracic surgeon, specialising in surgical conditions of the heart and chest. Although at first the heart surgery I performed was carried out in adults, I soon found myself operating on babies and young children with complicated heart defects. This was enormously challenging and rewarding although, with young children of my own at the time, it could be particularly upsetting when one of my little patients died.

At the same time my adult thoracic practice, dealing with all other conditions in the chest apart from the heart, was growing considerably. There came a point when I realised that I could not give sufficient attention to both the children and the adults in different hospitals five miles apart, and I had to make a choice. Both were extremely demanding of my time, energy and intellectual effort. There was a danger that I could not give sufficient attention to detail in every case and I might miss something. It also occurred to me that I could have my own heart attack before the age of forty-five if I continued to work intensively in two such high pressure branches of the specialty.

In 1979 I decided to concentrate full time on adult thoracic surgery and gradually developed a very large practice in all sorts of diseases in the chest. I was sorry to leave heart surgery behind because I had been trained in it, had carried out some exciting research in the United States and had initiated some important developments in the United Kingdom. I had, however, prayed quite hard about it and felt that I had made the right decision. The rest of my career was to confirm this.

It was then that lung cancer began to play an important part in my life. Every week I would see between five and ten new lung cancer patients in my various clinics in Liverpool, Warrington and the Isle of Man. It gradually became clear to me just how much lung cancer there was in the region. It also became devastatingly obvious how little I could do for these patients.

Surgery was, and still largely is, the only hope for cure for people with lung cancer and yet only one in ten of the patients referred to me could be considered operable. The remainder would die, half of them within a few months and most of them within three years of diagnosis. Even among those I operated on, thinking there was a chance of a cure, half would not survive five years. The overall survival rate for lung cancer was therefore in the region of five per cent and this figure had not changed since King George VI died of lung cancer in 1952.

The situation was unacceptable. A concentrated effort was required.

Chapter 3

Up Against a Brick Wall

I will never forget the day or the time. It was a dull, cloudy afternoon on Wednesday, 18 April 1990. The meeting started at 4 o'clock. I was sitting in my office at the Cardiothoracic Centre in Liverpool with my secretary Sheila Christian and one of my patients, Eric Morris. Sheila had had some experience with the Pain Relief Foundation at Walton Hospital and Eric was a businessman who had become a good friend and supporter since I had removed his lung for cancer two years previously.

I outlined to them my concerns about the huge problem of lung cancer in the North West of England and about the complete lack of any fundamental research into the disease in our universities and hospitals. I felt we had a great opportunity and therefore a responsibility to make a significant contribution to our understanding of the development of the disease, its prevention and eventual elimination. Cases of lung cancer were present in large numbers in our community: the answers must also be there. They just needed to be found.

I proposed to Eric and Sheila that we should establish a new charity, wholly dedicated to the study of lung cancer in all its aspects. I set out the objectives of the charity and these have remained virtually unaltered to this day. Considering we had neither money, nor institutional support, our aims were very ambitious.

I proposed that we should set out to support a basic science research programme into the molecular biology of lung cancer, looking into the genetic changes which occur in the lung during the development of a cancer. Having attended a science lecture in Toronto in 1986, I realised the importance of combining this type of research with epidemiology, which studies trends and risk factors in different populations and individuals.

We would tackle the problem of cigarette smoking – the most common cause of lung cancer – but this would have to wait since there was already a great deal of activity in this area by government and other organisations, whereas there was virtually no basic scientific research being carried out anywhere in the country.

As a doctor dealing every day with lung cancer patients, I was anxious to improve facilities for them in terms of nursing care and access to the latest technology and forms of treatment. We would not, however, undertake anything which ought to be done and paid for by the National Health Service.

All this without a penny in the bank, no influential patrons, no Trustees or charitable status and no track record of fundraising! I must have explained it well and with sufficient conviction to Eric and Sheila because they immediately agreed to support me. I was elected Chairman, Eric became Treasurer and Sheila was appointed Secretary.

We also agreed on a name. Our new charity would be called the Lung Cancer Fund and we retained this name until about a year after Roy Castle died. It was simple and to the point – describing exactly what we were about – raising money for lung cancer. My son, Philip, designed a logo for us with the sun, representing the charity, coming out from behind a cloud, representing lung cancer. Our corporate colours would be blue and yellow.

But why form a new charity? Why not simply approach one of the established local or national charities instead? The problem was that none of these appeared to be interested in lung cancer and, writing this fifteen years later, they still put very little money into basic scientific lung cancer research, although it remains the most common form of cancer and within five years kills ninety-five out of every hundred people affected by it.

I had, in fact, recently made a formal application to the British Lung Foundation. I was at that time a committee member of the first regional branch of the BLF which had been set up in the North West by Dr Colin Ogilvie, probably the best physician I ever came across in my long career and a member of the central grants committee of the BLF. Colin encouraged me in my application and was as disappointed as I was when it was turned down.

The application had been for funding to appoint, within the University of Liverpool, a Senior Lecturer in Thoracic Surgery with a special interest in lung cancer. It would have been the first appointment of its kind in the country and would have stimulated an intensive lung cancer research programme. It had been approved at the highest level by the University but they had no money, the Health Authority had no money, the hospital couldn't help and now even the British Lung Foundation had turned me down.

Faced with this brick wall, I decided that I would raise the money myself. The sheer scale of the problem of lung cancer was so great that

I felt strongly that it deserved a charity of its own, particularly as the other cancer charities were doing so little to combat the disease. The profile of the disease had to be raised. The public and those in a position to influence public policy had to be made aware of the seriousness of the situation.

Lung cancer up to this point had been the forgotten cancer – the Cinderella cancer – and most people, even many patients, had negative attitudes towards it. It was a disease on the whole of poorer people; the prognosis was hopeless and those affected did not live very long; and, above all, it was generally seen as being self inflicted. Patients sometimes felt guilty because they had smoked and unfortunately this guilt complex was confirmed by some of the doctors and other professionals looking after them. Collectively they had no voice and no one was beating on the door of government demanding something should be done.

The stock response to any discussion about the disease, which still pervades many corridors of power and medical circles, was that all that needed to be done to cure lung cancer was to stop people smoking. I made myself unpopular by insisting that this was a very inadequate response and nothing more than an excuse not to put valuable resources into lung cancer research.

My first argument was that, by the Government's own figures, there would still be millions of people smoking for decades to come and lung cancer would therefore afflict many thousands of people for the foreseeable future. In addition, more and more people were being diagnosed with lung cancer even after having stopped smoking. A lung cancer policy which only aimed at stopping people from smoking did nothing for this large group of patients who had heeded the health warnings, stopped smoking, and yet still developed lung cancer.

Moreover, there were several hundred people in the UK every year who got lung cancer, never having smoked in their lives and we couldn't ignore these.

I made the point also that, as an advanced nation, we had the resources – the technology, the scientists and the disease itself – to come up with the answers for the developing countries who were currently being blitzed with tobacco advertising and promotion and would inevitably come into their own lung cancer epidemics in due course.

Vital though it was to do everything possible to stop people smoking, this was not enough, so far as lung cancer was concerned, for the reasons given above. An intensive research programme was required to investigate the other risk factors which determined why only certain people who smoked got lung cancer and to study the development of the disease in the lung in order to identify the early changes which occurred, so as to allow much earlier diagnosis and therefore better chances of cure.

I was not a trained research scientist. I did have an academic background in that I had published a lot of papers and contributed to the advancement of my speciality, but I was not a cancer scientist. And yet I was highlighting deficiencies in cancer science and setting up a cancer charity which would have a strong research bias.

This would cause jealousies and difficulties in acquiring credibility for the charity in the scientific community. Who was this surgeon in Liverpool who was trying to point the way forward in lung cancer science?

I pressed on regardless.

Chapter 4

Point Zero

We had nothing but an important idea and a determination to make a difference. We were at point zero. The thought of failure never occurred to me, although I had no idea how far we would get. With a certain amount of bravado I chose the figure of £1million as our objective and put up posters in the hospital corridor publicising the Fund and seeking donations. There were a few cynical smiles around at that time but I had a certain prestige and popularity and was able to carry it off.

The Chief Executive at the hospital suggested that I should put the money raised into one of the endowment funds of the Health Authority. I resisted this and was determined to keep the Fund fully independent of any Health Service administration, since I had seen the difficulties which could be caused by this type of arrangement.

There were only three Trustees, Eric, Sheila and myself. I began immediately to recruit others. I sought the help of my senior colleagues first of all and Dr Peter Clark, oncologist, and Dr Chris Evans, chest physician, agreed straight away to help. We needed legal help to establish the Fund on a proper footing and to achieve charitable status. Tony Twemlow, a senior lawyer in Liverpool, accepted my invitation to become a Trustee. Brian Case, a golfing friend and an accountant with Touche Ross, came on board and Kevin Murphy from Lloyds Bank joined us and was elected Treasurer.

From very early on, therefore, we had a solid group of respected individuals whose expertise in various areas I could call upon. Doctors, on the whole, do not make good businessmen and I needed around me people who could make sound business decisions about organisation, budgeting and investment, so I was pleased when Bill Matthews, Regional Director of Barclays Bank in Liverpool also became a Trustee.

From the beginning I tried to find people who had specific expertise and could take from me responsibility for those aspects of the work of the Fund in which I was weak: finance, public relations, research, fundraising, tobacco issues and education. It could be said that there was little left after these but I did have some strengths.

I had a clear vision of the direction we should take although I did not know the limits we could reach. I was able to articulate this vision and to motivate others to join the campaign and put their hearts into it. I had organisational and writing skills and an ability to communicate and keep everyone informed. Perhaps most importantly I had determination and perseverance. Nothing would ever make me give up, no matter what difficulties we encountered along the way.

Perhaps my greatest source of strength was my patients themselves. They were my prime motivation and every day, in my clinical practice, I was reminded of the devastating effects of lung cancer on individuals and their families. I didn't hesitate to tell my patients about the Lung Cancer Fund and donations and offers of help began to come in.

The very first donation was a cheque for £100 from a patient from whom I had removed four different lung cancers over a period of ten years. Tom Guest was a master butcher who used to tell me as he went to sleep under the anaesthetic that his job and mine were very similar! I thought it would be very appropriate if he were to be the first contributor and he willingly agreed. Both he and his wife became strong supporters of the Fund until he died several years later.

We had our first £100 and I remember clearly the day we reached a thousand. All great things have small beginnings and we were on our way towards that £1million. By now, George Millington was helping on a voluntary basis. His wife, Iris, was a patient of mine with small cell lung cancer and both of them became fully committed to the cause. George kept the books and also did his own bit of fundraising. He would go round the city libraries leaving stocks of bookmarks giving information about the Fund. Although, sadly, Iris died the following year, George has remained a loyal friend and supporter to this day and I have had many occasions to be grateful to him for dealing with difficult situations.

Lord Brookes was our first patron. Ray Brookes had been Managing Director, President and then Life President of GKN, a large engineering firm based in the Midlands. He had retired to the Isle of Man and was seventy-nine years old when I met him. He had developed lung cancer and was referred to me for diagnosis and treatment. From the beginning we got on remarkably well and I told him about my plans for the Fund. He promised to help and he persuaded Sir Michael Bishop, Chairman of British Midland Airways and Lord Cholmondeley, Lord Great

Chamberlain of England to become patrons with him. I am pleased to say that he survived for fifteen years following surgery; valuable years which he spent travelling, fishing and attending the House of Lords. Throughout this time he remained very grateful for what I had done and gave me tremendous personal support.

We now had a Board of Trustees and three very distinguished patrons but very little money in the bank. We had no track record of fundraising, research, or any other achievement, so that my powers of persuasion must have had some merit. It did demonstrate, however, the powerful case that there was for a lung cancer charity and I will always be enormously grateful to this group of experienced, hard-headed and intelligent individuals who grasped what I was saying and gave it their support.

It now became easier to approach other prominent people to become patrons and we soon had a very impressive list. Night after night, on coming home from work, I would sit at my word processor composing letters and documents highlighting the serious nature of the problem of lung cancer and pleading for help. Fortunately, my wife, Elizabeth, was very tolerant and encouraging as she has been ever since and her understanding and friendship were important in sustaining my commitment. Despite this, there have been many times when she has said, "Why did you ever start this?"

By the end of 1990 much of the groundwork had been done and we had reached the stage when we would soon be ready to launch the new charity into the public arena.

Chapter 5

In the Spotlight

2 May 1991 – the day chosen for the public launch of the charity. Two hundred people attended a buffet lunch in the main boardroom of Barclays Bank Regional Head Office in Liverpool. It was one of the best gatherings for such an event ever seen in the city.

We owed much to the publicity given to the launch by the *Daily Post*, the regional morning newspaper, which produced a four page centre pull out on the day and which had adopted us as their charity a few months before. Brian Case had taken me to see the editor, Keith Ely, and I had sat in his office and passionately told him what I was trying to achieve. Although the *Post* did not usually give its backing to any particular appeal and although, at that time, we were still embryonic as a charity, Keith said he would support us and from that day on our credibility was enormously enhanced.

Media support is vital for the success of an appeal and to have the public backing of a major newspaper was very encouraging. This put us firmly in the public spotlight and we were never again to leave it. It would reach its highpoint with the involvement of Roy Castle.

Ken Dodd and Libor Pecek, principal conductor of the Royal Liverpool Philharmonic Orchestra, did the honours and in their different ways gave us the start we needed. Ken Dodd looked at the beautiful ceiling in Barclays Boardroom and said that he hadn't realised that the launch was going to take place in Derek Hatton's front room. He also said very shrewdly that £1million would not be enough. To me that had seemed like a realistic first target but at the next Trustees' meeting I told the Trustees that our aim should be to raise £1million each year for the next five years. They looked at me rather oddly but time would show that Ken Dodd had been right.

Libor Pecek spoke eloquently and said that he was ashamed that we were trying to raise £1million for lung cancer when the Royal Philharmonic Society was trying to raise £6million to refurbish the concert hall. Both Ken and Libor had given me something to think about but I have always had the facility to pick up on important points and suggestions made by other people and incorporate them into my own thinking. It was all a matter of growing and learning

The launch was the first time that I met Lady Pilkington. She was brought along by Brendan Carroll, who was helping us with public relations. She brought with her a donation of £5,000 which thrilled me to bits. She was to become a very good friend and far and away our most generous benefactor. I was very fond of her and she never refused me if I asked her for help. The magnificent way in which she was to set the Roy Castle Cause for Hope Appeal going will be told in a later chapter.

Lady Mavis was widely known and respected for her charitable work and affectionately dubbed the Queen of Merseyside. To have her on our side was a major step forward for the Lung Cancer Fund.

A few days later I received an anonymous donation for £18,000 and it felt as if we were really on our way. The publicity surrounding the launch had been exceptional. Granada covered the story and carried an emotional but down to earth interview with Iris Millington. Radio Merseyside, Radio City and the other local press also carried the story.

Over the years I have come to be familiar with appearing on television and the radio and to dealing with journalists although I have never become very comfortable with it. It has, however, been essential to the progress of the charity and the media have invariably been friendly and supportive. We have much for which to thank them. It intrigued me though that, whereas I could take someone's lung out in the most difficult and dangerous of circumstances, I could yet get extremely nervous in front of a microphone.

My first ever radio interview was a recorded ten second slot on Radio City for a news item and I can still remember the shaking in my voice and the sheer terror of trying to get my brain to send sensible messages to my tongue. However, within a few months I would be operating live in front of several television crews – carrying out an operation which had never previously been performed – and all for the sake of publicising the Lung Cancer Fund!

I have several times been an innovator and one of my principles has been to start small and to let things grow naturally. I was determined that the Fund would only grow at a pace which we could control and this would necessarily be relatively slow in view of our lack of experience and the huge commitments I had in other parts of my life, especially my surgical work. We started therefore with a limited view of the area in which we would raise funds and spend them. Several times the Trustees and Brendan Carroll suggested that we should launch out nationally and my reply was always the same: "We'll do that when the time is right, let us grow naturally and it will be obvious when we should become a national charity". This proved to be a sound approach and, in due course, when Roy Castle came along, we had a very firm basis on which we could rapidly expand. And what a difference Roy made!

For the moment, however, we confined ourselves to Merseyside, Cheshire, North Wales and the Isle of Man, the area covered by the Regional Cardiothoracic Centre at which I worked and which contained something like 3.7million people. It was enough to be going on with and at that time seemed ambitious enough for me.

I had been visiting thoracic surgeon to the Isle of Man since 1977 and had acquired many good friends and patients on that lovely island. I wanted the residents of the island to benefit from the activities of the Fund and one of my patients, Dr Douglas Mellon, became a Trustee. Douglas was a retired haematologist who had introduced blood transfusion to Ireland.

I decided that we should launch the charity on the Isle of Man soon after the launch in Liverpool, and on 14 May 1991 we held a lunch in the presence of the new Lieutenant Governor, Sir Lawrence Jones and his wife, Lady Brenda, who had agreed to become a Patron of the charity. It was a well attended event and I was by now becoming used to speaking in public about our aims and objectives. Little did we know that four years later Sir Lawrence would become a patient of mine with lung cancer and die the night before he was due to leave the island at the end of his term of office. I am never surprised, however, by this type of thing, because there is so much lung cancer in our community and the prognosis is so poor. It was still very sad.

A committee was formed on the island, led by Peter Vanderpump who is still Chairman today and has given over fifteen years of loyal, painstaking and invaluable service. The powerhouse on the committee in the early days was Eunice Salmond, later awarded the MBE for her charitable work. Eunice was then a senior journalist on the island and a formidable woman with phenomenal fundraising abilities, full of ideas and energy and not willing to take no for an answer. She was also a smoker. One of the first things she did was to stop smoking and to give the money she raised in sponsorship of this to the Lung Cancer Fund.

Mildred Cooper, whose husband was also a patient of mine, later became President of the Lung Cancer Fund on the Isle of Man and over the next few years did a magnificent job with Peter and the rest of the committee in raising over £300,000 for the charity. Mildred knew at first hand the devastation which lung cancer can cause and, with great energy and commitment, has persuaded her large circle of friends and admirers to support the charity, frequently allowing her beautiful home to be used for fundraising activities.

A new charity will always ruffle a few feathers and provoke some jealousies. Established charities and particularly their volunteers and supporters, can feel threatened and in danger of losing valuable income. I never worried about some of the things which I heard were said about us since I was convinced that there would be no need for the Lung Cancer Fund if others were giving lung cancer the attention it deserved. I also resolved that I would never speak badly about any other charity and would always respect the freedom of people to support whichever charity they wished. Now that the Roy Castle Lung Cancer Foundation is firmly established this is not often a problem but it certainly was when we were small and just starting out as the Lung Cancer Fund.

By the middle of 1991 the fledgling organisation had firmly taken root. We had enough money to employ our first fundraiser, Isobelle Weatherill, and in the summer of that year my daughter Catherine joined us to give secretarial support. Catherine remained with the Fund for over four years and was an absolute stalwart in the early years of the appeal. She was very popular with volunteers and patients alike and related well to the media, which was becoming steadily more important to us as we developed. Catherine was a steady influence and presence during the early uncertain years and I could always rely on her in spite of her very typical teenage social life!

We now had charitable status, a strong Board of Trustees, an impressive list of Patrons, the support of the *Daily Post* and of Lady Pilkington, who would later become our first President. We had employed our first staff and money was beginning to accumulate in the bank. Much had been achieved but we were still only just beginning. I had a lot to think about as I continued with my very heavy workload as a surgeon and tried to contribute as much as I could to my family life. I also used to pray a lot which gave me great strength.

Chapter 6

Staple Gun Surgeon

'Staple Gun Surgeon' was the headline in the *Today* newspaper on 4 October 1991. 'New keyhole lung surgery successful' said the *Daily Telegraph*. 'Glimpse of History Through a Keyhole' was the title of a two-page spread in the *Daily Post*. The story was covered by *The Times* and most of the other national newspapers and I even subsequently received cuttings from papers in New York and India. Television and radio coverage was extensive.

The purpose of seeking all this media activity was to give publicity to the Lung Cancer Fund. I had a difficult decision to make and knew that I was putting my professional reputation on the line. But my motivation was to highlight the problem of lung cancer and to make people aware of our new charity which was the only one anywhere in the world wholly dedicated to the study of lung cancer.

It is a dangerous thing for a surgeon to court publicity and when he or she does this for their own benefit it is to be deplored and rightly condemned. I wondered if people would understand and whether I might even end up having to explain myself before the General Medical Council! I decided, however, that this was an opportunity which could not be missed. After all I was about to perform an operation involving the latest surgical technology and which had never been done before. My view was that in order for a charity to be successful in the modern age it had to be prepared to embrace the media, since this was the route to millions of potential supporters and donors.

There was also the risk that the operation could fail. Perhaps something disastrous would happen, particularly as this was the first operation of its kind. I needed to be very sure of the techniques I would use and of my ability and experience. I would also need a very special patient.

For years I had been used to looking inside the chest with telescopes to make a diagnosis and to take biopsies without opening the chest. I had also built up an international reputation for the use of stapling instruments in chest surgery, having been one of the first to introduce them into the United Kingdom ten years earlier. I had written many papers and lectured widely on the subject. Earlier in the year I had been invited as Visiting Professor to the Royal College of Surgeons of

Canada to lecture on my experience of using stapling instruments to remove the gullet for cancer and other conditions.

The first crude instruments were developed in Russia. They were designed to apply staples instead of stitches by the mechanical action of the instrument, sealing off or stitching together parts of the lung or bowel. The early Russian models were efficient but very ponderous and slow to use. Each staple had to be individually loaded on to the instrument by the scrub nurse and this would take a lot of time. The instruments were heavy and cumbersome to handle.

One day a visiting American surgeon was shown them in action by one of his Russian colleagues. He immediately saw the advantages and smuggled one of them out of the country as he returned home. American designers, with an eye for a vast new market, soon improved the efficiency and handling qualities of the instruments. Easy loading cartridges were the first feature to be introduced and eventually the whole unit came complete from the factory and was even disposable. A cutting knife was incorporated in some designs so that tissue could be stapled and cut at the same time. This was to prove the vital breakthrough in the design of instruments to be used in what came to be known as Keyhole Surgery.

In 1987 the first gallbladder was removed using keyhole techniques and further abdominal and gynaecological operations became commonplace with this new type of surgery. No one, however, had yet developed instruments which were suitable for keyhole use inside the chest.

For several years I had been invited to visit the United States to advise one of the companies developing stapling instruments on the design of new instruments. In April of 1991, I was invited to a seminar in New Jersey and was the only European surgeon present. The topic was the possible use of stapling instruments in keyhole chest surgery.

On returning home I performed an 'endoscopic assisted' removal of a lung cancer on a wonderful seventy-five-year-old lady from the Isle of Man, Phyllis Broadbridge. Although not truly 'keyhole', the incision was much smaller than normally used and the dissection had been carried out looking through a fine telescope. The stapling instruments however were still bulky and a moderate incision was required to insert them into the chest. Phyllis did very well and was back playing golf within a few weeks. *The Times* covered the story and Phyllis made several television appearances, publicising the Fund, and took part in a marvellous photoshoot with Norman Wisdom. She remains well to this day. The real thing, however, was yet to come.

Ramsey Dickens, or Mack as his family and friends called him, was referred to me in September 1991 with a shadow on his chest X-ray. It was not very large and was on the edge of the lung. It was a new shadow and had the appearances of a cancer. He was sixty-eight years old and in good condition. All tests for spread of the tumour were negative and he therefore appeared to be an excellent candidate for surgery. His attitude to his condition was excellent. He was intelligent and calm, understood everything that was said to him and was confident in the ability of those looking after him. His family was as solid as a rock and hugely supportive.

Autosuture (UK) had just received delivery from the United States of the latest design of stapling instrument for use inside the chest. When I spoke to them they readily agreed to let me have a supply for use in Mack's operation and I therefore spoke to him and explained what I had in mind. I told him that this would be the first time that such an operation had been done and I described to him the technique and also the likely benefits. A tiny incision should mean less post-operative pain and fewer chances of complications. I also assured him that I would immediately revert to a standard operation and open up the chest widely if, at any time, I was unhappy about the progress of the operation.

Mack gave me his full consent and we were ready to go. It was then that I had to make the decision about publicity and I thought long and hard about it. Eventually, after talking again in detail with Mack, I decided that we would make an announcement ahead of the operation in order to attract maximum media interest and the most remarkable day of my surgical career was about to take place.

Thursday 3 October 1991 was the date set and media presence on the day was extraordinary. BBC, ITV, Sky TV, as well as journalists from local and national newspapers, were all invited into the operating theatre and mingled with nurses, anaesthetists, junior doctors and representatives of the Lung Cancer Fund. Every one of them behaved impeccably. GMTV featured the story in the morning programme TV-AM and both Mack and I had already done several interviews before the start of proceedings.

The operation began mid-morning. I had decided to carry out another operation first, using the new stapling instruments in a keyhole operation to remove a cyst from the lung of a young girl, Kelly Mason, who was a highjumper and in training for a place in the Olympic team. This had gone well and I felt fairly confident.

My first task was to wipe out from my mind all the people and television cameras in the operating theatre and to concentrate completely on the job of removing Mack's lung cancer. I also had to put to the back of my mind the possible consequences of anything going wrong but this is a common task for a surgeon.

With television cameras in front of me, behind me and at the top of the table, I made the first incision, 2cm long. I then inserted the telescope and found the tumour which showed up on a monitor ahead of me. I had a good look around the chest to check for secondary deposits, enlarged lymph glands or other abnormalities, but all seemed well. Through a separate incision I inserted the staple gun and applied it to the lung at the side of the tumour. It kept slipping but eventually I got it in place and fired it. There was no bleeding and a portion of the lung separated from the tumour.

Several more applications of the instrument gradually encircled the cancer. Each application had become progressively more difficult as I cut deeper into the lung and I had in mind all the time that I might have to open the chest and call a halt to an historic operation. It was taking longer than I expected and, although the TV crews were getting anxious about their lunchtime news schedules, they never said a word but wandered noiselessly around the theatre taking shots from all sorts of angles.

Eventually the cancer came free but I then had to get it out of the chest. The incisions I had made to insert the instruments were just too small and I had to extend one of them by about a centimetre but I was happy to pay that price. The tumour came out complete with a margin of healthy lung all round and I breathed a sigh of relief behind my mask. I looked again inside at the lung and the staples had worked well. The lung was not bleeding and the cut edges looked secure and airtight.

I quickly sewed up the incisions and turned to go to the sink to take my gloves off and wash my hands. It was then that the TV crews broke ranks a little. The operation had taken longer than expected and they had their deadlines. We had planned a press conference in the Lecture Theatre but this would be too late for them if they were to make the lunchtime bulletins.

As I turned away from the operating table I found a microphone in front of me beside a TV camera. "How did it go, Mr Donnelly?" "Was it more difficult than you expected, Mr Donnelly?" "Are you satisfied, Mr Donnelly". I did my best to answer concisely and politely but I was mentally and physically drained and it wasn't easy. However, if it gives the Fund good publicity, I thought, I'll keep going along with it. Reporters were doing the wind up for their pieces in the theatre and journalists had their questions to ask. It was a time for a cool nerve and a clear mind. My main concern was for Mack who was just beginning to come round from the anaesthetic but all seemed well with him – he was in good hands.

The theatre soon cleared and Mack woke up safe and well. He smiled and asked how things had gone. He was reassured by what I had to tell him. His recovery was remarkably quick which I put down to the fact that he did not have the effects of the usual 35cm incision. He was interviewed by the TV reporters sitting up in bed within a couple of hours of the end of the operation and that evening we both did a live broadcast from his bed on the BBC *Look North* programme.

I went home that evening satisfied with the result of the operation and very happy about the publicity which had been generated for the Lung Cancer Fund. On the way home, at about 9pm, I called into the studios of Radio Merseyside to do a live interview for BBC World Service. We were making real progress.

Chapter 7

Smokefree Liverpool

During all of this excitement we passed the £100,000 mark and began to put a structure into our affairs by establishing Finance and General Purposes, Grants and Fundraising Committees.

Bill Matthews expressed the view to the Trustees that we had to become a national charity if we were to meet our objectives and raise substantial donations from trusts and the corporate sector. We began this process by applying to the Charity Commission to remove from our registered name the designations Merseyside, Cheshire, North Wales and the Isle of Man.

I still felt we were too small and inexperienced to assume national status and that we needed to grow a bit more first before we could do that. We did not have on board the personnel to run a national charity and I certainly did not have the time to give to the demands which would result. However we would from now on have an open mind about it and await the right time and opportunity.

As a result of the publicity surrounding Ramsey Dickens' operation I lost a good friend and close colleague from the Board of Trustees. Dr Chris Evans, a highly respected chest physician, felt that it was inappropriate for a doctor to attract media attention in the way that I had done, although he recognised that I had not done it for myself but to attract attention to the charity. A few days after the operation he sent me a letter of resignation as a Trustee which saddened me because he was a good friend and had a huge amount of wisdom and knowledge to offer our development.

Chris had been my Vice-Chairman and in his place we appointed Brian Case who was to give many years of dedicated service to the charity as a Trustee. He later became Chairman of the Remuneration Committee when this was established and a long standing and valuable member of the Finance and General Purposes Committee. He was also responsible for establishing and chairing an *ad hoc* committee which reviewed the operational structure and procedures of the Fund.

A lot of good things were happening about that time. For instance I met Terry Malone, who intended to run up Snowdon and raise £1,300 for the Fund. He came to the hospital and we agreed that the money would be used to provide a counselling room in the outpatients department. Terry said that he was touched by the thought of the emptiness that some people must feel when they are told that they had lung cancer. "Some of these people are living on their own and not particularly well off, they have to leave the doctor in clinic and get on a bus and the shock must be unbearable."

Terry was expressing my own thoughts exactly and soon that room would be available for patients and their relatives to recover after their interview with the doctor and to be counselled by a specialist support nurse. Terry subsequently became a Trustee and Chairman of the working party overseeing the development and building of the Roy Castle Research Centre.

We set up an Association of Friends with Ken Dodd as president and over forty celebrities agreed to join this. One of them was Richard Baker who at that time was the senior newsreader on BBC television. He came to Liverpool to introduce a concert by the Royal Liverpool Philharmonic Orchestra, conducted by Libor Pececk. This was sponsored by Lady Pilkington and raised a significant sum for the appeal.

Jean Boht and the cast of the television programme *Bread* were in town and came to visit the hospital. I took them around the wards and they cheered the patients up immensely. Jean has remained a wonderful friend since then.

Donations continued to come in, large and small. Eric Morris and his friends arranged a glittering ball at the sumptuous Grosvenor Hotel in Chester and a group of nurses from the hospital took part in a sponsored swim which raised £759. Everything helped and slowly the bank balance grew bigger but it was still rather slow considering how much we wanted to do.

The issue of children smoking came up for the first time. I said publicly that in my opinion it was a form of child abuse to sell cigarettes to children, to encourage them in any way to start smoking and even to set them a bad example by smoking in their presence. This language seemed extreme to some people at the time but these were the lung cancer patients of the future and I had seen enough of the real thing to feel very strongly that our children deserved better.

When the Lord Mayor of Liverpool came to visit the Cardiothoracic Centre I said that the aim of the Lung Cancer Fund was to "eradicate lung cancer completely from our community and to ensure that our children and our children's children are spared this appalling scourge". I was just beginning to understand the role of the tobacco companies in the recruitment of children into a lifetime habit which would eventually kill at least half of them.

In December 1991, I was invited to address a full sitting of Liverpool City Council on the problems of smoking in the city, which I had begun to highlight. At that time the Council had its own problems and, when I arrived, all the members were milling around outside the chamber. The sitting had been suspended because of disorder, the police were involved and I was due in next to speak to them!

Rosie Cooper, Deputy Lord Mayor, chaired the session and in her blunt, no nonsense manner brought the proceedings to order. Without referring to my notes I gave an impassioned speech, detailing the horrendous statistics of smoking related illness and mortality in Liverpool and how the Council had a great responsibility to the citizens for whom it was responsible, especially the children, to tackle the issues in a forthright and determined way.

One member stood up and said he had never heard better arguments to stop smoking and that he was determined to stop straight away. Well at least I had one convert! The general response, however, was good and the Council subsequently set up a Tobacco Abuse Working Party in collaboration with the Health Authority. The Council has remained supportive of the Fund since then and later donated the site on which the Roy Castle Research Centre was to be built. Several smoking prevention initiatives developed over the next few years, starting with the Tobacco Abuse Working Party and culminating in the Smokefree Liverpool campaign to ban smoking from all public places in the city. It is safe to say that Liverpool has led the way in the variety and originality of smoking prevention schemes and the remarkable collaboration that exists between the Council, the health authorities, the Roy Castle Foundation and all other interested organisations.

The end of the year came with us still uncertain of what lay ahead and still learning how to run a charity. We were, however, gathering momentum and maintaining our enthusiasm for the cause. Our profile was significantly higher but this would bring with it greater expectations.

Chapter 8

The Most Frightening Words in the English Language

In 1992 the pace really picked up and several developments important for the future character of the Fund took place. We had a number of setbacks but there was also the introduction into our thinking of several initiatives which would have a major impact on the rapid expansion and blossoming of the charity into what it is today. It was also the year in which Roy Castle developed lung cancer and we began to think about how we might be able to involve him in our plans.

The year began with the loss of our first fundraiser, Isobelle Weatherill, and during the course of the year we appointed two more in her place, both of whom proved to be unsatisfactory and moved on. We felt the need for an effective, high quality head of fundraising who could make a major commitment to the charity and bring in the substantial funds we required in order to achieve our ambitious aims. But such people are few and far between and my time was repeatedly taken up with fundraising and PR activities of one kind or another.

During the year we also parted company with Brendan Carroll who had been advising us on public relations. This was an expensive item and the Trustees felt that we should look after these matters ourselves in-house. Much of this fell back on me and, with the comings and goings of three different fundraisers, I was very glad to have my daughter Catherine to share the load, which she did cheerfully and effectively.

Iris Millington died in May. She had been very special and, with George, supported me superbly. She had small cell lung cancer like Roy Castle but had survived five years after I had operated on her. I went into her room to see her shortly before she died. I had done a minor operation on her and was able to reassure her that it had gone well. She smiled and her last words to me were, "My hero!" I left and she died peacefully during the night. George was devoted to her and was devastated by her death but became even more dedicated to the Fund. Over the years he has been a good friend and helped me through some very difficult moments.

Sheila Christian retired as my secretary at the hospital and resigned as a Trustee. She had been there with me from the beginning and I was sorry to lose her but she was not going to find it easy to continue her involvement. She had done a good job.

Some personality clashes between Trustees led to some lively meetings which I had to chair and meant that I was to lose one of the newer recruits and later another but not before both had made significant contributions at a time when the Fund was determining its operating structure. Both have remained friends and take pleasure in the success which the Fund later achieved.

****

We began, that year, to hold events in London starting with a lunchtime reception at the House of Lords. Lynda Chalker, who would later become Baroness Chalker and contribute so much to the success of our World Tour in 1997, attended her first function as Patron and I had the opportunity to explain to her the aims and objectives of the charity.

The House of Lords event was the first time I met Faith Brown. I had only previously known her by her stage image and, when it was suggested that I should have my photograph taken with her for the *Daily Post*, I wondered if it was the right thing for me to do. After all, I had my surgical reputation to protect and suspected that my rather conservative colleagues would consider that I had gone too far this time, mixing with stars of show business and gaining publicity from it. Faith was a wonderful personality and became a good friend of the charity and, as usual, was wearing one of her dresses which gave prominence to her natural features!

I decided that I would go along with it for the sake of the Fund, as I did on many subsequent similar occasions, and let my surgical work speak for itself. I am sure there was a fair bit of chattering behind my back but I lost no friends and they kept referring their most difficult patients to me. This was only right because, despite the demands made upon me by the charity, I continued to give my full commitment to my clinical work and to teaching, training, lecturing, administration and travelling abroad to conferences and scientific meetings of various kinds.

I was Director of Research and Education at the Cardiothoracic Centre in Liverpool and would later become its Medical Director. I was also Chairman of the Medical Research Council working party on cancer of the oesophagus, a member of the national executive of the Society of Cardiothoracic Surgeons of Great Britain and Ireland, Postgraduate Tutor in cardiothoracic surgery for the University of Liverpool and an examiner for the Royal College of Surgeons. I was invited to operate in Cairo and Kuala Lumpur and was the first European member of the American Thoracic Surgical Club. I had my hands full and family life with my wife and five children was very important to me, as was my prayer life. My golf tended to suffer and my handicap gradually went up.

****

I was now beginning to propose to the Trustees projects for which the money being raised could be used. It was time for us to begin to achieve some of the objectives we had been talking about from the beginning. Even now the Trustees were cautious and I had to press hard to convince them to release the funds, since they would have liked to have continued to build up our reserves. I felt that we had to have some record of achievement to present to people who were giving us money and I was impatient to get started with our programmes. This would become a recurring theme.

Firstly I proposed to them that we should provide funding for a lung cancer support nurse at the Cardiothoracic Centre, which dealt with hundreds of lung cancer patients every year. I had seen the real need for such a person in every clinic I held. As things were, I would sit down with a patient and their relative and gently tell them that they had lung cancer and what I proposed to do. As soon as the words lung cancer were mentioned I could see their eyes glaze over and, no matter how kind and considerate I tried to be, it was obvious that they were taking in very little of what I said. One of my patients explained it to me by saying that, in his view, the words 'lung cancer' were the two most frightening words in the English language.

After I had finished talking to them, the patients would leave the consulting room, perhaps with tears in their eyes, walk out past all the other people waiting in outpatients, and go to stand at the bus stop. They would then go home, close the door, sit down and only then would the full impact of the diagnosis hit them. They would then have a dreadful wait before going back into hospital for further tests or treatment. It could be a very lonely and distressing time.

I wanted a nurse who would sit in clinic with me, listen to what I said and, when I had finished, take the patient and their relative out to the counselling room provided by Terry Malone and sit down with them over a cup of tea. She would then ask them if they had fully understood what I had said to them and explain it to them if they had not. When they had composed themselves she would let them go but would give them her telephone number so that they could ring her when they got home, if they had any other questions. They could also ring her at any other time until they came into hospital and she told them that, when they were admitted to the hospital for surgery or investigation, she would come and see them and ensure that they were all right. She would become a friend, a friend with professional expertise, who would accompany them throughout the course of their illness and treatment, liaising on their behalf with doctors, Macmillan nurses, surgeons, oncologists and social workers.

This would be a completely different and far more humane way of treating people and the Trustees agreed the funding. This would be the first lung cancer nurse of this kind anywhere and within a couple of months Pauline Dixon was appointed and patients immediately felt the benefit of her caring and competent approach. We would go on to fund five lung cancer support nurses around the UK and provide support to a network of about 350 other lung cancer nurses who have come into post in recent years funded by the NHS.

****

I had by now dropped the idea of appointing a Senior Lecturer in Thoracic Surgery, which had been my first ambition when setting up the charity. The University wanted too much money deposited in their trust funds to finance the post for fifteen years. In addition, the surgeon would have had to spend a significant amount of his time in teaching and administration and in treating patients with other conditions apart from lung cancer. It did not seem to be the best use of our money but I was still determined that we should fund an intensive laboratory research programme because there was very little of this being done anywhere and the need was urgent.

It was then that I met Dr John Field, now Professor Field. I had put out feelers in the University and, in what I later came to recognise as typically fast action when possible grant funding might be available,

John knocked on the door of my office at the hospital at 12 noon on 1 February 1993. He introduced himself and talked about his research ambitions. His background was in genetics and he had been working at the University Dental School for several years, having developed his own small laboratory to study the genetic characteristics of head and neck cancer. He was clearly extremely bright and organised; a hard worker with an impressive list of publications. I also liked him a lot and we shared an easy, and at times very flippant, sense of humour.

Throughout the development of the Lung Cancer Fund and later the Roy Castle Lung Cancer Foundation, I have been continually impressed by the fact that the right person has turned up to meet a particular need, someone with outstanding qualifications for the job in hand, at a time of life when they could make the maximum contribution. Roy himself was an example of this, as was Sylvia Ingham, our first Chief Executive, and indeed the idea to start the whole thing had come at a stage of my career when I had the experience and prestige to make it happen. It was also remarkable that when Roy died we had Fiona, who, in her own special way, would make such a contribution to our success. These and many other examples are too many to be pure coincidence and I can only assume the influence of Providence.

In no time at all John Field had submitted his first grant application to study the early genetic changes occurring in the lung during the development of lung cancer. After taking advice from cancer scientists outside Liverpool, who reviewed John's application for scientific merit, I put it to the Trustees, but the well was not yet deep enough to draw the large amount of money required to fund this work and I had to tell him to be patient and to reapply the following year. John is now Director of Research for the Roy Castle Foundation with a budget approaching £1million a year.

* * * * * * * * * *

Lady Pilkington officially became President in September and Les Howell, Graham Brown and Anthony Hannay became Trustees, adding business, financial and legal expertise to the Board. Nicholas Wainwright, of jewellers Boodle and Dunthorne, ran our Christmas card campaign and received one unsolicited donation of £25,000, a very sizeable amount for us at that time. The support groups on the Isle of

Man and the Wirral continued to be very active and at the suggestion of Eddie Pope, a golfing friend of mine, a new group sprang up in Aughton and Ormskirk led by Roger and Jean Healey.

A very successful Lunch and Auction was held at the Hyatt hotel in London. This was organised with the considerable help of Geraldine and Stewart Jamieson. Geraldine had interviewed me in depth a couple of times on Manx Radio and had subsequently given me tremendous support. She and her husband were very well connected and Geraldine was good friends with many prominent individuals and personalities who had been guests on her programme.

Lord Cholmondeley came to the lunch as well as Robert Powell, Trevor Brooking, Alec Bedser, Moira Anderson and other celebrities. Among the items for auction were a racehorse, a diamond necklace and a cricket bat signed by Sir Donald Bradman and Harold Larwood. Lady Pilkington, who had donated the necklace, bought it back for a considerable sum – her generosity knew no bounds. Altogether a large sum of money was raised for the Fund.

****

Most importantly, that year, John Brocklehurst became a patient of mine. John was to be the catalyst who triggered the idea in my mind of a purpose built research centre given over entirely to the study of lung cancer. John was an experienced businessman and used to seeking grants from public funds. First of all we put together an application for European funding to build and equip a molecular biology (genetic) laboratory in the University and John Field had co-operated in preparing this.

The application was unsuccessful but some time later John Brocklehurst told me about the very large amounts of European funding which would come into the region over the next few years as Merseyside was declared an Objective One area. He asked me if I could think of some capital project which could qualify for this money and I put together the ideas for what became the Roy Castle International Centre for Lung Cancer Research. I had always intended to fund various aspects of lung cancer research in different departments of the University but, although my intention was always to ensure that the several departments worked together, it seemed to me that this would be done much more effectively if they were all housed together under one roof. The building could also house the headquarters of the charity.

****

About this time we began to work with Quadrant, a marketing company based in Warrington to whom we had been introduced by Bill Matthews, one of our Trustees. They were full of ideas, especially Lynne Bell with whom we mostly dealt. They came up with proposals for a region-wide street poster campaign, highlighting lung cancer issues and statistics and advertising the Lung Cancer Fund.

It was Lynne Bell and her colleagues who came up with the strap line 'Cause for Hope' which we immediately adopted because it seemed so appropriate.

The ideas for the poster campaign were good but expensive, even though they felt that they could get poster sites for nothing, or at least very low cost. The idea was to use a picture of a celebrity with a message and some facts about lung cancer and the charity. It was proposed that Richard Baker, the BBC newsreader, should be shown with the caption 'Now for the good news'. Jean Boht's picture would appear with the appeal 'Give us the Bread' referring to the television comedy series *Bread* in which she starred. Finally Lynne said that she would approach Roy Castle to take part with the message: 'Forty thousand people die each year from lung cancer. DON'T BE PASSIVE'. Roy agreed and thus came into our lives.

Chapter 9

Two Very Special Patients

One Sunday night in July 1992, the telephone rang and woke me up. Elizabeth answered and I heard her say, "Do you know what time it is?" She passed the telephone over to me and it was the general practitioner of Archbishop Derek Worlock. "His Grace has been coughing blood up over the weekend. He went to the Royal Liverpool Hospital and had an X-ray but they couldn't see anything. He's still bringing up little bits of blood – what should we do?"

The Archbishop was a very powerful and prominent man, not just in his own church, in which he had an international reputation, but also in local and national politics. I was wide awake now and suggested that His Grace should come to the Cardiothoracic Centre first thing the following morning when I would be doing a clinic in outpatients.

We shook hands and he sat down opposite me in the consulting room. He had been feeling tired and unwell and had begun to cough small amounts of blood whilst returning late at night from an engagement a couple of days before. He had not smoked for almost thirty years.

When I looked at his X-ray I knew that something was seriously wrong. Part of the lung was lying collapsed behind the shadow of the heart which was hiding it and the reason that the less trained eye had not seen it at the Royal. Obviously there must be a lesion blocking that part of the lung which was responsible for the bleeding. This might be a benign tumour, a foreign body, or a cancer. I had to look down with a bronchoscope and find out.

After my clinic was over I performed the examination under general anaesthetic. I found a tumour lying in the orifice of the lower lobe of his left lung. It was not obviously benign or malignant and I took a biopsy. He received the news very calmly and I agreed to see him at home in a couple of days with the result.

The pathologist rang me to tell me that it was a small cell cancer of the bronchus, the most aggressive and lethal of the different types of lung cancer. Very few are suitable for surgery but occasionally they are operable if no evidence of spread outside the lung can be found.

I went to the Archbishop's House on the Wednesday morning to give him the diagnosis and to discuss treatment options. His reaction was very pragmatic. He was a deeply emotional man but hid this from all except his closest friends and advisors. He once told me that listening to *You'll Never Walk Alone* would sometimes make him cry. I couldn't tell how the shattering news I had just given him affected him. We discussed what should be done next and I told him that he would need a variety of scans and blood tests to determine whether the cancer had spread to other parts of his body.

That afternoon he was due to deliver the oration for Grace Sheppard, wife of Bishop David, for an Honorary Fellowship at Liverpool John Moores University. He was determined to go ahead with this and, so as not to spoil the occasion for Grace, he told neither her nor her husband of his condition, in spite of his very close friendship with them both. Afterwards they said that they suspected something because he looked unwell but he performed in his usual eloquent manner and the afternoon went off well.

The scans and other tests were clear and I consulted with my chest physician and oncology colleagues. The tumour was localised in the lung and we all agreed that I should proceed to remove it. After the Archbishop had recovered from the operation, and if all was well, he would then have an intensive course of chemotherapy. I conveyed this to him and he gave his consent.

By now the press had got a sniff that something was happening, although they never knew the serious nature of the diagnosis until a formal announcement was made. It was not surprising, however, that suspicions that he was ill leaked out, since he was one of the most prominent people in Liverpool and was visiting various hospitals for tests. He was annoyed about this and reluctant to give much information but something had to be said, not least because he was due that week to lead the Archdiocesan pilgrimage to Lourdes and he was due to be admitted into hospital for surgery on the day that the pilgrimage left Liverpool. A press release was issued saying that he was going into hospital for surgery for a serious lung condition and it was immediately after the event that I insisted that we should let people know that he had cancer, since I felt it would be impossible to talk sensibly to the media and hide the fact.

I went to see him in his room before he was taken down to theatre. He gave me a blessing and, although he didn't say anything, I am sure that his well-developed sense of humour would make him appreciate the advantages of this to him personally.

In theatre I first explored his neck for malignant glands but found none. I could therefore go ahead with the operation and, with some trepidation because of his high public profile, opened his chest. The tumour was moderately big but free from attachment to any other organs and there was no evidence of any spread inside the chest. As I held his lung in my hand I had a real sense of spiritual awareness, of responsibility for the life and health of one of the senior prelates of the church who was held in such high regard by people of all denominations (and none) and who had done so much to bring the churches together. I prayed that God would guide my hand.

The operation went well and his recovery was rapid. The nurses were sorry to see him leave. A month later he was well enough to begin chemotherapy under the expert care of Dr Peter Clarke. This was a very difficult period for him and he suffered a great deal. From the surgical point of view he made good progress but the complications of chemotherapy took their toll and distressed him considerably. He insisted however on going out in his car and visiting one of his parishes every week.

By December, the chemotherapy had finished and his first formal visit back to his Cathedral since the start of his illness was for Midnight Mass. I was there and could only admire the courage and fortitude of the man. He was still thin and weak and leaning heavily on his staff but he endured the whole service and even preached, although, for the time being, his voice had lost its former strength.

During his stay in hospital I talked with him about many things and told him about the Lung Cancer Fund. I asked him to become a Patron to which he agreed. Later the Trustees would appoint him Vice-President of the Fund. I suggested to him that he should speak out publicly about lung cancer and be a voice for all the thousands of people in the region who developed the disease but did not have the same opportunity as him to be heard. This appealed to him and he willingly accepted the role.

He lived for four years more and was a constant and loyal supporter of the Lung Cancer Fund. When Roy Castle became involved they corresponded and became friends. The Archbishop had great admiration for Roy and drew spiritual inspiration from him. When he preached at the Venerable English College in Rome in 1994 he spoke about Roy, of his courage and his faith and acceptance of God's will. He told of how Roy's deep faith and sense of mission shone out like a bright light, a lantern of joyful hope. He held Roy up as an example to the trainee priests to whom he was talking.

Shortly before his last admission to hospital I sat on the side of the Archbishop's bed at his home in Liverpool and spoke about Roy and especially about his cheerful and uncomplicated acceptance of God's will for him. Roy would say that he didn't want to die but if that was what God wanted then it was all right by him. "You get on the bus and you trust the driver," was his way of putting it.

Derek Worlock had always been a man of political influence and power and he found it very hard to give this up. It was his way of life and his natural talents were perfectly suited for the life he had led. He was terminally ill but still felt that he had much to offer and was deeply concerned that all his work might be undone after he was gone. I believe he eventually came to terms with this but the simple and uncomplicated approach of Roy Castle to illness and death undoubtedly helped him in his final struggles. I was pleased to have played some part in bringing them together.

* * * * * * * * * *

She was only twenty-four and very beautiful. She was full of life and so popular that her colleagues called her 'the wild thing'. She was a cabin flight attendant with Loganair and loved her job. She had never smoked in her life and she got lung cancer.

While on holiday in Guernsey with her friends she had felt pain in her back and shoulder. One day she coughed up some blood and went to see her doctor who referred her to a local specialist. Probably because of her young age and the fact that she was a non-smoker it took some time to make the diagnosis and other more likely things were considered first. When the specialist looked down into her lungs with a bronchoscope he could see abnormal tissue in her right bronchial tubes and took a biopsy. This was reported as showing cancer and, within a few days, Nicola Lawrence was sitting opposite me in my clinic with her father.

Bright, cheerful and with a very positive attitude, she could hardly believe that she had lung cancer. Surely that was a disease of old men! Well, perhaps it used to be, but things have changed and the number of women getting lung cancer is rising: in fact in some parts of the country it is even more common in women than breast cancer. But she had never smoked and there was no smoking in her home where she lived with her parents and sister. It was difficult to blame passive smoking because no one in her family smoked, nor any of her close friends, and smoking was not allowed on Logan Air flights.

We never did find out why Nicola had developed lung cancer although we suspected a drug which she had been taking for acne over the previous six months and which had been associated with a few reported cases of various bizarre kinds of tumours. We will never be able to prove it unless more similar cases get reported in the future.

Nicola had been referred to me in the hope that she would be suitable for surgery and I immediately arranged to bronchoscope her myself and organised several diagnostic scans. Her bravery and lovely smile will always stay with me, as will the tremendous loving support given to her by her family in the difficult months that lay ahead.

The scans showed that her cancer had spread outside her lung and I had to tell her. I didn't hedge around the subject but, as sympathetically as I could, I sat on her bed and told her that she could not have surgery. She had desperately wanted this but she was a very definite and determined person and it would have been wrong to have given her false hopes, or not to have told her the truth. I did however give her some hope in that I was going to refer her to one of my colleagues for radiotherapy and/or chemotherapy.

Her attitude amazed me. She was obviously stunned and distressed but from the start decided that she was going to put up a fight and face the cancer head on with whatever was required. So many patients have won my admiration for the way in which they bravely accept their diagnosis and get on with fighting it but, at twenty-four, it must be much more difficult. "I'm going to beat this ugly little thing inside me," she said.

Even at that time when she had every right to do nothing else but think about herself and concentrate on getting well again, she told me that she wanted to help the Lung Cancer Fund. She knew that she was different from most lung cancer sufferers and that she would have a good chance of persuading her friends and colleagues to raise money for the Fund if she asked them. It was obvious that her youth and beauty and lovely personality would attract widespread sympathy and support.

I also knew that it would give her something else to think about whilst she underwent some very unpleasant treatment. Some patients find that this helps them a lot. This was the case with Roy Castle and it was certainly true of Nicola. She told Jill Palmer of the *Daily Mirror*, "I have never done anything like this before but I want to find out why someone like me can get lung cancer. I wanted to make an effort to do something. This seemed an ideal way. I can only live one day at a time but I don't want to waste one of those days. This will help keep me going, give me something positive to think about and do."

The most important thing was to get on with her treatment but in those few moments, when everything seemed utterly bleak, the Nicola Lawrence Appeal was born. Friends, family and colleagues at work rallied round and it was obvious how much they loved her and wanted to help her achieve her ambition. In addition to raising a large sum of money, Nicola was to be the one who first persuaded Roy Castle to take a real interest in the Lung Cancer Fund.

It was Lynne Bell of Quadrant who suggested bringing Nicola and Roy together. Nicola had always been a fan of Roy and jumped at the idea of meeting him, especially as he had also developed lung cancer. She was already undergoing treatment and felt quite unwell. It was unlikely that she would be able to make the journey by rail or even by car but to fly down would be very expensive and even that would necessitate a long drive from Heathrow to Gerrards Cross where Roy lived.

We had taken on Eddie Pope to develop Nicola's Appeal and Eddie had an ability to get round any sort of problem. His range of contacts was amazing and he would not hesitate to use them. He had a soft voice and caring nature and a capacity to sweet-talk anyone to help a worthy cause. I saw several examples of this during the time that Eddie was with us and on this occasion he persuaded the owner of the Cheshire Flying Club to fly Nicola and Lynne free of charge to Denham airfield near Roy's home. Amanda Williamson of the *Daily Post*, who had become friendly with Nicola and her family, went with them.

It was Nicola's birthday and, in typical fashion, Fiona had prepared a birthday cake. Nicola was tired and felt unwell but was absolutely thrilled to meet Roy, who was well at the time, and they joked and laughed a lot. It meant a great deal to Nicola to meet her hero and she was very happy. She told Roy about the Lung Cancer Fund and about her Appeal and Roy promised to help her.

She returned home elated that Roy had agreed to help and overjoyed at meeting him and Fiona. However, the journey home was a long and distressing one. The weather was bad and Nicola felt so ill that they had to make an unscheduled stop at Birmingham to allow her to recover. It was late when she finally arrived home but, determined young woman that she was, she felt it was all worth while and so it was.

Nicola was never able to take much part in the fundraising activities of her appeal because of her condition. She had to go through radiotherapy and chemotherapy which used up all her energy. Some days she was unable to get out of bed. "I just wish I could go to work," she said, putting to shame all those of us who complain about having to go to work.

Nicola died in February 1993, just four and a half months after I first met her, and at her funeral service I gave the following address

I first met Nicola Lawrence a few short months ago when she came to the Cardiothoracic Centre with her mother and father. She was a little apprehensive but immediately you could see those wonderful aspects of her character and personality which I and many others would come to know so well. She was bright and cheerful, she was beautiful, she was intelligent, she was brave and she was very determined. "I'm going to beat this thing" she said. "It's smaller than me!"

It was clear to me from that first consultation that the problem was very serious and I had to tell her that we could not operate. This was devastating for her but she reacted as she reacted to every setback and piece of bad news she received during the course of her illness. Within moments her cheerful courage reasserted itself and she faced the situation as it was, without pretence but with great determination. "I'm going to beat it," she would often say and I could only admire the spirit of one so young.

Without hesitation she put herself in the hands of the doctors, nurses and others who looked after her so expertly from then on at Clatterbridge Hospital. She endured radiotherapy followed later by chemotherapy as her disease progressed but she never complained and tried to hide the distress caused by her symptoms. Only those close to her knew what she was going through and many times our hearts went out to her parents Pamela and Colin and her sister Suzanne who cared for her with such great devotion and love. Very sadly, not even Nicola, with all her great vitality, courage and determination, could 'beat it' and we lost a very special person last week.

Nicola did however, leave behind a wonderful legacy, a legacy of a life

well lived and lived to the full and, in the last months of her life, an inspiration to me and to many others, both now and in the years to come, to intensify our efforts to eradicate the scourge of lung cancer from our community. She willingly and freely gave her name to the Nicola Lawrence Appeal which is a special appeal on behalf of the Lung Cancer Fund to raise sufficient money to establish a senior research position in the University of Liverpool to investigate the causes, prevention and treatment of lung cancer.

Nicola was enthusiastic about her appeal right to the end and only regretted that she could not do more personally because of her ill health. Her many friends and her colleagues at Logan Air rallied round her and have worked hard raising money in Manchester, Glasgow, Guernsey and Liverpool. She once said, "The one thing I would really like to do is to get out of bed in the morning and go to work." She truly loved her job with Logan Air and will be sadly missed. Her story has received national attention in the press and on television. Touched by her beautiful personality and courage in adversity, people have responded from all over the country with donations and offers of help.

Nicola will never be forgotten. Her life was short but of immense value. She often said, "I don't want anyone else to go through what I am going through." This must continue to be our ambition and Nicola will always be an inspiration to me and all who work with the Lung Cancer Fund. Nicola was positive, optimistic and determined and that is how we will always remember her and how we will keep her memory alive as we go about our task of promoting and developing the Nicola Lawrence Appeal for the benefit of many thousands of people. We thank God for her life and, now that her suffering is over, may she rest in peace with Him.

Nicola's appeal continued for twelve months after her death. Family, friends, staff at Logan Air and sister airline Manx Airlines raised well over £100,000. Rather than putting the money to fund a research position for three years, her mother and father agreed to my suggestion that it should be used to build and equip the library that was to be an important element in the plans for the Roy Castle Research Centre.

The Nicola Lawrence Library is now an integral part of the Centre. A lovely picture of Nicola in uniform hangs outside the door and will be a permanent reminder to all visitors and users of the library of a very special young woman.

Chapter 10

Ball of Fire

In early 1993 we were working hard with Lynne Bell and her colleagues on the street poster campaign. The Trustees went along with my request for funding although some of them were concerned about the overall cost, a recurring theme between me and the Trustees! I could see advantages to the Fund quite separate from those directly linked to the lung cancer messages. We needed to keep the publicity machine going and the involvement of three celebrities, whose profile was high at that time, would certainly help in this respect. I wanted especially to establish closer links with Roy Castle.

We invited Roy up to Liverpool to launch the poster campaign and to record a message to be played to anyone telephoning in response to a free phone number which would appear on the posters.

On 31 March 1993, I had my first meeting with Roy at the Albert Dock in Liverpool, the site chosen for the launch of the posters. Media interest was considerable and it was my first opportunity to see Roy at work with children and with the press, radio and TV. My vivid recollection is of his easy, cheerful manner and broad, spontaneous smile, all of which he retained even when he became very ill later on.

It was impossible not to get on very well with Roy as many thousands of people would verify and I was no exception. He was relaxed, easy to be with, looked you straight in the eye and listened carefully to what you said. At that time he was thought to be in remission from his cancer but as the day went on I became worried about him and my clinical sense suggested to me that all was not well. He had a troublesome cough and appeared flushed and I wondered if he had a temperature.

After the launch we went to the Adelphi Hotel for a celebration lunch. We were joined by Lady Pilkington, some Trustees and friends of the charity. Speeches were made and we gave Roy a clock as a memento. Looking back this seems an extraordinary present to give someone with cancer but he seemed unperturbed and Fiona told me some years later that she still had it at home.

I then took Roy to the Cardiothoracic Centre where we toured the wards and operating theatres. I was used to taking civic dignitaries and others around the patients but this was different. Whereas they tended to fall into a pattern of questions, which they would ask every other patient, Roy had something individual to say to each one. He always found something funny to say, something unique to each one, which made them feel that Roy Castle had really visited them personally.

Many photographs were taken and there was a lot of laughter. For a few precious minutes those patients, suffering from a variety of conditions, including lung cancer, forgot that they were in hospital. They also had something exciting to tell their relatives and friends when they visited that evening. Roy had brought real joy into their lives and I was very impressed with him. Although he was not well himself and had travelled a long way, he gave himself unstintingly to those people and for a while took away the pain of being ill and in hospital. I was to see much more of this selfless generosity of spirit before he died.

It was in the office of the Fund at the Cardiothoracic Centre that he recorded the message responding to callers from the poster campaign and asking them to be generous. He had to do it several times because of his cough but he persevered until it was right.

I saw him off in the car we had arranged for him, not knowing when we would meet again but sure that we had made a good friend, who had developed some understanding of what kind of people we were and of what we were trying to do. At the time, however, I am sure that he still saw us as just another charity that he could help and there were many of those.

About this time Robert Powell also became involved. His father had died of lung cancer and I wrote to him asking him if he would become a patron of the Fund. He agreed and has subsequently become a very close friend and supporter of the charity to the extent that the Epidemiology Laboratories in the Roy Castle International Centre for Lung Cancer Research were named after him.

****

In May the Trustees approved a grant of £140,000 to Dr John Field of the University of Liverpool to investigate the early genetic changes occurring in the lung during the development of a lung cancer. Although we had raised £333,000, this was a sizable award to give only two years after the setting up of the charity. To my mind, however, this was, without doubt, the most important area of lung cancer research and one which was being almost completely neglected elsewhere. We have subsequently given increasing levels of grant to Dr Field and his research now forms the core activity of our research programme.

* * * * * * * * * *

I continued to work on my ideas for a research centre wholly dedicated to the study of lung cancer, though it could be nothing more than a dream at this stage, bearing in mind our income which, though very respectable for a new charity, would take many years to reach the levels needed to build such a centre, never mind equip and run it.

Archbishop Derek Worlock, who was my patient at this time, was supportive of the idea and did the old trick of asking me to put my ideas down on one side of a sheet of A4 paper. I did this and he was impressed, not an easy thing to achieve! He began to introduce me to some businessmen who might be able to take the project forward but it was clear that the key to any significant progress was the fundraising campaign which would be needed to support it. None of us had the ability to raise the sort of funds required.

During the spring and summer the Trustees had been debating how we could develop into a national charity which could raise the money we would need if we were to meet our general objectives. A development plan was prepared and this highlighted the need for a Chief Executive and a structure which put in place actions and financial procedures which would ensure the integrity of the Fund during a period of rapid expansion.

In the weeks that followed the posts of Chief Executive and Treasurer were clearly identified and individuals nominated to fill them. After first accepting, they both withdrew for personal reasons and we were back to square one. As a busy surgeon I also had my hands full at this critical time in the development of the Fund. There was vigorous discussion at some of the Trustees' meetings and, at one point of honest debate, Les Howell asked if I was the right person and had the necessary qualities to be promoting the charity! This was actually a good and important question and I was pleased when the Board responded in a positive fashion, although my own answer would have been less certain. Doubts were expressed whether we were all on a wild goose chase and could ever achieve our objectives but generally the Trustees were very supportive and we managed to keep things on an even keel. However it was a time of great change in our thinking and, as Founder and Chairman, I had to ensure that we continued to move forward, albeit cautiously and carefully. I prayed a great deal in those days.

****

It was then that a significant event in the history of the charity took place. We recruited Sylvia Ingham. I had known about Sylvia for about a year. Eunice Salmond on the Isle of Man had told me about her and had suggested that I get this 'ball of fire' to organise an event for the Fund. Eunice had come across her during Sylvia's visits to the island on behalf of Border Television's Telethon campaign and had been very impressed.

One day, in the middle of June 1993, Eunice read a small piece in the *Daily Telegraph* saying that Independent Television was winding up its Telethon fundraising campaign after several successful years. She immediately realised that Sylvia would be looking for a new job and rang me that morning since I had told her we were looking for someone with exceptional fundraising ability.

Sylvia was in her office at Border Television when she received my call out of the blue. She told me that her mother had died of lung cancer and, before she died, they had together raised £1.5million for a scanner for the local hospital in Cumbria. She expressed a keen interest in what we were doing and she agreed to come down to Liverpool to meet me and talk things over.

We met outside the Metropolitan Cathedral and I took her into the city centre to the Athenaeum Club for lunch with Eric Morris. We did not eat much but talked at great length. I told her my vision for the Lung Cancer Fund including my idea for an international lung cancer research centre.

Both Eric and I were convinced that here was the fundraiser we were looking for. As Eric said to me, "She can do it for you", and Eric was a very hard-nosed, experienced businessman. Sylvia appeared bright, imaginative and energetic, prepared to make a serious commitment, because of her mother, to the battle against our common enemy, lung cancer.

Within a week or two Sylvia Ingham had been interviewed by a delegated group of five Trustees, all of whom were unanimous that we should make every effort to secure her services. Comparisons were made with salary levels in other charities and I was authorised formally to offer Sylvia the post of Head of Fundraising for the Lung Cancer Fund, recognising that some negotiation would be required to compensate Sylvia for working away from home.

I was surprised and disappointed to receive a letter from Sylvia a few days later turning down the offer on the basis that, having discussed the matter with her family, she had decided that she did not want to take another high pressure job so soon after finishing with Border Television.

This time I asked Eric Morris to ring her and try to persuade her to reconsider. Eric had suffered from lung cancer and was passionately committed to the charity. He also felt, as did we all, that Sylvia was the person to take our fundraising to a level commensurate with our medical and research ambitions. He spent forty minutes on the telephone discussing, negotiating and cajoling.

The main stumbling point turned out to be not so much her salary, or the intensity of work, as the problem of working for a Liverpool based charity while living in Cumbria. Eric proposed to the Trustees a small increase in salary and expenses to cover her stay in Liverpool for those days during the week when she would be in Liverpool. The Trustees agreed and Sylvia started working for the Lung Cancer Fund on 8 September 1993.

****

At the same time accountants Touche Ross were appointed to carry out a detailed treasury function and business controls review of the charity which was presented to and accepted by the Trustees at their November meeting. An important recommendation of this report was that the Trustees should delegate more day to day management to a Management Executive and that a Chief Executive should be appointed. Rather than take on an additional high salaried person and because they thought that she had the ability to do the job, the Trustees appointed Sylvia Ingham as Chief Executive in addition to her role of head of fundraising. In retrospect this was a poor decision because Sylvia's strengths lay in imaginative and dynamic fundraising initiatives and she never enjoyed the responsibilities which came with day to day management.

I continued to be very hands on in my dual role of Chairman and Medical Director of the Fund but I was very happy to see the formation of the Management Executive since I was very much aware of my limitations and lack of business management experience. I would happily have stood down at any time as Chairman but the Trustees wanted me to continue since they felt that my public profile and day to day commitment benefited the charity.

I felt reasonably secure in carrying on since we had a strong Board of Trustees and the Management Executive comprised, in addition to myself as Medical Director (not as Chairman), the Treasurer John O'Brien, who was a senior partner of KPMG and Terry Malone with his experienced and practical business brain. Sylvia was meant to chair this group as Chief Executive but was not used to doing this and leadership came from the other members, although Sylvia contributed fully in her own area of expertise.

****

During all these changes I had a job to do and a busy practice to maintain. I travelled extensively and during the year went as Visiting Professor to Athens, Cairo and Kuala Lumpur to operate and to lecture on keyhole surgery in the chest and the use of stapling instruments in thoracic surgery. By this time, with the help of some brilliant young doctors from the USA and other countries, I was beginning to add substantially to the scientific literature through the publication of a series of original papers on the result of these techniques and other topics.

In every respect, things were hotting up and I had great hopes for the future of the Lung Cancer Fund but I had no idea of the explosion of the charity on to the national scene which was about to take place through the involvement of Roy Castle and the PR skills of Sylvia Ingham.

Chapter 11

Concrete Proposals

I continued to push my ideas for a lung cancer research centre and, by the time of the Trustees' meeting in October 1993, a working party had been set up comprising John Brocklehurst, previously mentioned in Chapter 8, Keith Hackett, a city councillor with a brilliant brain for securing grants, Sylvia Ingham, who attended very few meetings because of other commitments, Stephen Quicke, a local architect who had been involved with the development of the prestigious Albert Dock complex in Liverpool, Eric Morris and myself.

Sadly, Eric's health was deteriorating and he had to resign from the working party and from the Board of Trustees. In addition to being a patient of mine and bravely battling against two forms of cancer, Eric had been one of the original three Trustees and a totally committed campaigner and worker for the Lung Cancer Fund. Eric was to die not long afterwards and everyone who has ever benefited, or ever will benefit from the work of the charity, owes him a huge debt of gratitude for the tireless work he did in helping the charity to get established. I will always miss him and will never forget him.

Eric's place as a Trustee was taken by Terry Malone, who had raised a substantial amount of money for the Fund, including the refurbishment of the counselling room at the Cardiothoracic Centre. Terry's strength of character and sound business principles made him an ideal Trustee and he was appointed chairman of the working party. For the next four years he project managed the development of the research centre to a successful conclusion and did a superb job.

We had still not committed any financial resources to the project but at their November meeting, the Trustees agreed to appoint accountants KPMG to write a business plan. At the same meeting Stephen Quicke addressed the Board and presented preliminary sketches and ideas. He suggested three possible sites in Liverpool, including my own hospital, the Cardiothoracic Centre, and the rapidly developing dockland area but my own strong preference was for a site adjacent to the University, since I had seen similar initiatives struggle because of their distance from the academic centre.

Stephen's preliminary drawings included all my ideas for the centre

– the disciplines of epidemiology, molecular biology, and pathology as well as a lung cancer library, a state of the art lecture theatre and the headquarters of the charity, which would manage not only our fundraising and accounts but also our smoking cessation and patient care activities.

John Field would join the working party later and contribute enormously to the detailed plans for the laboratories and other academic facilities.

We now had concrete proposals at an early stage of planning but the scheme would cost over £3million to build and equip and we had less than £500,000 in the bank. It seemed impossible.

Chapter 12

Let's Go for It!

Soon after Sylvia Ingham joined the Lung Cancer Fund, her father developed lung cancer. This was an extraordinary turn of events, particularly as Sylvia's mother had previously died of lung cancer. Ray Wanless was a fit man but was reluctant to undergo any tests or major treatments. Sylvia brought him down from Cumbria to see me and within a week or so I had operated to remove the cancer and he had made a good recovery. He was to have a further twelve months of good quality life before the cancer struck again.

This was a major distraction for Sylvia as she began her new job but, because of the nature of her father's illness, she became even more determined to make a success of it. She soon began to show her talent and the Lung Cancer Fund moved up several gears.

Sylvia was surprised at the size of the network of celebrities and supporters who had already pledged themselves to the charity and she began to work energetically on this and develop it. Her first major initiative was to persuade her previous employers, Border Television, to release for a week, at no cost to the charity, a team of experienced journalists and cameramen to make a video to promote the Fund. Ian Fisher, Eric Scott Parker and Alan Turn were to be key players, although no one realised it at the time, in a pivotal development for the charity, the recruitment of Roy and Fiona Castle.

In planning the video, Sylvia arranged to take the team down to London where they intended to interview Robert Powell and Jean Boht, having already filmed Ken Dodd in Liverpool. She also intended, if she had time, to go and see Roy Castle although, when she spoke to me, she was not sure that she would be able to do this. I remember vividly looking her in the eye and telling her that she must go and see Roy, that he was probably the most important person to be included in the video in view of my knowledge of him following the street poster campaign earlier in the year. Fortunately she listened to me and history was made.

* * * * * * * *

Early in December 1993, Sylvia and the Border team knocked on the back door of Roy and Fiona's house in Gerrards Cross. It was snowing.

In Sylvia's words, a beaming, bouncing Fiona opened the door with a big smile. "Roy's not very well but he doesn't want to put it off – he wants to do it. He's resting in bed but if we get organised he will come in." Apparently Roy had been undergoing tests and they were expecting a call from the specialist.

The crew set up in the lounge, they had coffee and Sylvia told Fiona about her dad. When Roy came in he appeared normal apart from an irritating cough as he spoke. After some general chat they began to film. Then the phone rang.

It was the specialist and Roy took the call. The cancer had recurred. "So what does that mean?" asked Roy. The doctor told him that he would require another course of chemotherapy, though not as severe as before. "Well, we fight on," said Roy.

He then continued with the filming as if nothing had happened and everyone there, with the exception probably of Fiona, was amazed. The video is still available today and in it Roy talks about his disease and his chances of survival and how children wrote to him saying, "We like you on Record Breakers, please don't die." When all the shots had been taken, Sylvia and the others drove away feeling very sad.

When she returned to Liverpool, Sylvia said to me, "We must do something big." The research centre was the obvious choice and we began to discuss how to involve Roy in this. We agreed that we would put Roy's name on the laboratory in the Centre if he would support us in our appeal. Later, after discussing it with the University, we would put his name on the whole building. But the immediate question was how could we enlist Roy's support to build the world's first international lung cancer research centre?

Ian Fisher helped Sylvia draft a letter to Roy and Catherine faxed this down to him. Within minutes the telephone rang and Roy was on the other end. "Let's go for it", he said. "The doctor says that I may not live until the New Year, so, yes, you can use my name but I may not be able to do very much for you because I am not very well."

We were on our way! Neither Roy, nor we, had any idea of the scale of the impact which Roy would make upon the nation and the success which the appeal bearing his name would have. Fiona said later that, in Roy's mind, we were just another cancer charity which he could help but before long his commitment to the cause would inspire the whole nation in a most remarkable way.

We began straight away to plan the campaign. We needed a bright and attractive name for the appeal and I sat down with Hilary Berg, a PR consultant with Williams Barber and Bird who were advising us at the time, Sylvia Ingham and my daughter Catherine. We tossed a few ideas around and I suggested using the motto, 'Cause for Hope', which the Lung Cancer Fund had adopted in its early days.

It didn't take long to come up with the name 'Roy Castle Cause for Hope Appeal' which rolled nicely off the tongue and had a very positive ring about it. I also suggested a figure of £12million for the appeal which was, to some extent, plucked out of the air but which would allow the Lung Cancer Fund to build and equip the research centre as well as establish a sizable endowment fund to run the centre over the next few years.

We decided also to use the Lung Cancer Fund's logo of the sun coming out from behind a cloud. When Roy saw this later, he added some musical notes within the sun and this seemed very appropriate to me.

****

In view of what Roy had said about his health and also what I knew about small cell lung cancer, I was anxious to proceed as soon as possible. We didn't know how long Roy would be with us, or how long he would be able personally to contribute to the appeal.

Sylvia and I drove down to Birmingham on Boxing Day. Roy was appearing in Pickwick at the Alexandra Theatre and we were taking the architect's drawings of the proposed research centre and wanted to bring Roy fully up to date with our plans for the launch of the appeal and secure his co-operation.

When we arrived at the flat where they were staying we had to wait a little while before Fiona came down to let us in. She wrote to me afterwards to explain what had happened.

"The day you came to speak to Roy about the appeal, we had actually forgotten all about it and Roy was having a lie in when we got your phone call saying that you were down in the lobby. We decided there wasn't time to get Roy dressed which was why he greeted you in his dressing gown. We rushed round tidying the little flat, put the kettle on and laid out some coffee cups so that you would think you were expected and then I came to meet you downstairs and pretended that we always took that long to receive our guests!" The point is that

Roy had lived with these kinds of requests over the years and had never taken them too seriously, always doing what he could and I think he thought this was just another. Little did he know that it would consume us both and that it would become the most significant part of the end of his life."

We had no appreciation of this and were delighted by the warmth of the welcome from Roy and Fiona, who made us scrambled eggs to go with the coffee. They were both very interested in the plans, but their knowledge of lung cancer and of research was, at that stage, rather limited and it would be some time before they fully realised the scope and importance of what we were trying to achieve. We spoke about the history of the Lung Cancer Fund and its progress so far and discussed the ideas which Sylvia had for the launch of the Roy Castle Cause for Hope Appeal.

****

The date was Thursday, 24 January 1994. It was cold and dark outside and more than eight hundred people were queuing on the steps of St George's Hall in Liverpool, waiting to get in for the launch of the Roy Castle Cause for Hope Appeal. Earlier in the day we had held a national launch at the Hippodrome Theatre in Birmingham with Roy and Fiona, Lesley Joseph, Vince Hill and John Nettles. That had gone well and received extensive coverage but the launch in Liverpool was the big one.

It seemed to take forever for everyone to file inside St George's Hall and we were all amazed by how many people had accepted their invitations to be there. The place was buzzing with excitement and anticipation; everyone was waiting to see Roy and to welcome him to Liverpool. This was the night when a deep bond of affection was born between Roy and the people of Liverpool which would grow steadily over the next eight months and eventually be sealed two days before his death with the conferment on him of the Freedom of the City.

Lady Mavis Pilkington, President of the Lung Cancer Fund, came out of hospital in a wheelchair to be present and brought with her a magnificent donation of £50,000 to set the ball rolling.

Archbishop Derek Worlock, by now our Vice President, was also there and later spoke of his admiration for Roy and his support for the plans to build a research centre which would study the disease which had afflicted him.

Rick Wakeman played the huge organ as people stood around (there were too many to sit down) eating the buffet and drinking a glass of wine, all of which Sylvia had managed to get donated by Sayers the Bakers. *Here Comes The Sun* by George Harrison was played over the PA system before the speeches began.

Roger Phillips, a Patron of the Fund since the early days and a leading presenter on Radio Merseyside, carried out his MC duties with gusto and good humour. When he introduced Roy the place erupted and Roy appeared to be quite moved by the show of warmth and good wishes. His big smile shone out and he spoke briefly but with sincerity and humour about the task in hand. He had such an attractive personality which made everyone want to support him. Emotions were running high and would have been even more so if people had known that he was now back on chemotherapy, taking tablets to try and control the recurrence of his cancer.

When my turn came to speak I tried to put everything into perspective and to explain the reasons for and the importance of the campaign on which we were embarking. It was a daunting task and, spotting Mike Walker in the audience, the new manager of Everton, I said that at least I had an easier job than he had!

It was a hugely successful evening and Sylvia, Catherine and our small team had done a magnificent job. Much more was to follow in the weeks and months ahead.

Chapter 13

'There's Only One Roy Castle'

Two days after the launch Roy was on the telephone. He had received a call from Steve McColl, Director of Special Trains for British Railways. Steve had seen a small piece in the *Daily Telegraph* about the appeal and had contacted Roy to offer a vintage Pullman train for a few hours to raise money. Steve, who was from Liverpool, had suffered from cancer himself a few years previously and was a long standing admirer of Roy's.

Sylvia Ingham's creative talents immediately slipped into gear and she met Steve for lunch the next day. She knew that Granada Television had used a train to collect cheques during their Telethon campaign. "Can I have the train for three days to do a record breaking journey?" she asked an astonished Steve, who, nevertheless, quickly agreed, although recognising that there would be numerous practical difficulties to overcome.

Sylvia worked on the concept and developed the idea of taking the train through all the ITV regions in the country, linking in with the local TV and radio networks. It was a hugely brave and ambitious proposal and immensely imaginative. The downside was that it would take time to organise, and there was a real risk that Roy would not be alive when all the arrangements were in place. In the end it was a very close thing.

The support of the media would be crucial but Roy's personality and the way in which he dealt with the cancer which was killing him gave them one of the most poignant and moving human interest stories for many years. The *Daily Post* continued to support us strongly but, by now, our main support came from the *Liverpool Echo* under the editorship of John Griffiths, who was to prove an invaluable and loyal friend of the Foundation. The *Echo* has a long history of successful campaigning and its wide readership in the Merseyside area ensured widespread awareness of the project which was now called the Tour of Hope. Arthur Johnson was seconded to the appeal by the *Echo* and Arthur's vast network of friends and extensive experience in public relations made an immense contribution to the Foundation, not just for the tour but for the next few years as well.

Steve McColl worked on the logistics of moving a special train around the UK for 16,000 miles, visiting twelve major cities. Sylvia and her team continued to develop all aspects of the Cause for Hope Appeal but, in particular, she had the huge task of enlisting media support and commercial sponsorship for the Tour of Hope, as well as working on the vastly complicated programme of moving the tour party from town to town and arranging high profile welcomes at each of the stops.

****

One day in February Roy was playing the piano when he noticed that the fingers on his left hand were not working properly. He couldn't move his index finger and he remembered a friend of his who had been diagnosed with brain cancer after having difficulty playing the piano.

Roy reported his symptoms to the doctors and investigations confirmed that his cancer had returned and that there were two small secondary tumours in his brain. I had seen this many times before in patients with small cell lung cancer and was very concerned when I heard about it. He began another course of debilitating radiotherapy and chemotherapy but this did not stop him doing everything he could for the appeal. His dedication, commitment and determination were undiminished and his bravery shone through.

On Wednesday, 16 February 1994, Roy visited the site where the research centre that would bear his name would be built. At the time it was being used as an NCP car park, having been a derelict site since 1941 when the buildings on it were demolished by a land mine during the blitz of Liverpool. We had not yet acquired the land but we were reasonably certain that this was where the pioneering research into early detection of the disease which was claiming Roy's life would be carried out.

He was being interviewed by Tom Mangold for the BBC programme *Here and Now* which was following him through his illness. He knew that it was very unlikely that he would see the centre completed and, in fact, he never even saw it started but he was still upbeat and positive about the importance of the work which would be done there. That day it was cold and wet but Roy would later say, "I may not be here to see it, but the day the centre is opened there will be a big ray of sunshine beaming down on it."

****

Soon after this Roy came up to Liverpool for a lunch with John Moores and fellow directors of the Littlewoods Organisation. He actually broke off the treatment for his brain tumours to fulfill this important engagement which he attended with Robert Powell. Littlewoods had become enormously important to us and had agreed to sponsor the tour to the tune of £30,000 which would cover most of our basic expenses. More importantly than this, however, was the potential for all five divisions of the company to raise money for the appeal and, for this reason, the senior directors of the divisions had been invited to the lunch with Roy.

Harry Thomas was a key person in this. Harry was responsible at main board level for public relations for the entire company and had put his whole weight behind our campaign. He had formed a committee with representation from each of the divisions which would result in over £1million being raised by Littlewoods staff right across the UK.

The lunch was intended to cement this process and was a great success, almost entirely due to Roy's infectious personality and the double act which he played with Robert Powell, by which they both had everyone in tears of laughter. John Moores presided and many times afterwards spoke of that occasion. What seemed to impress him most was that Roy was able to make jokes even about his own death. Roy, with Robert, had won them over and when the tour took place in the summer the commitment of the Littlewoods staff guaranteed its success. In return we delivered massive publicity for them over a long period of time.

The Pools division of Littlewoods was to prove to be our most valuable source of income, not only that year but for several years afterwards, raising hundreds of thousands of pounds for us every year.

In early 1994 Littlewoods Pools had begun to be seriously affected by the National Lottery and were planning the launch of a new initiative using scratchcards to try to regain some of the revenue lost as a result of the impact of the Lottery on their football pools. Their strategy was to take advantage of two criticisms levelled at the Lottery, firstly that punters had no say in which good causes received the benefit of their £1 and, secondly, that a relatively small amount of each £1 found its way to the good causes.

Trish Dodd was Marketing Manager of the Pools division and was working closely with her General Manager, Phil Rooney, on the project.

Plans had been finalised and approved at Board level, with five charities chosen to benefit. These were national charities so as to be instantly recognisable. Punters would know when they chose a scratchcard which charity they would be supporting because it would be named on the card and they would also know that 20p in each £1 would go to that charity.

Through connections within the Littlewoods organisation, Sylvia Ingham managed to get a meeting with Trish and Phil. She told them about Roy Castle, the problem of lung cancer and our plans to build the world's first international centre for lung cancer research. By now we had artist's impressions of what the centre would look like and these were stunning.

All this was new to Trish and Phil and when Sylvia left they looked at each other and said, "We must include it". It was brand new and they had the opportunity to be in at the start of something which was going to be very big and important. They could see that it made commercial sense but it was so amazing that it was like a dream and they feared they would be received with scepticism when they presented it to their colleagues.

Soon after this I went to see them myself with Sylvia. We talked for so long that it began to get dark outside and Trish remembers being startled when the automatic window shutters came down.

In the next few days and at the last minute of their preparations to launch the project, they quickly rewrote the scratch card business plan to include the Roy Castle Cause for Hope Appeal for the Lung Cancer Fund, as an additional charity and this was approved by the Board of Littlewoods.

Roy was soon back at St George's Hall with Robert Powell to launch the scratchcard for Littlewoods. He looked in good form with his Roy Castle Appeal baseball cap and sweatshirt and people there said they would not have known he was ill, yet he had been having radiotherapy and chemotherapy and must have known that he did not have long to live. After the launch, Roy and Robert went on the *This Morning* programme with Richard and Judy and there were a lot of laughs. Roy managed to sell Richard a scratchcard on air. The publicity was superb.

We subsequently received millions of pounds from Littlewoods Pools, later called Littlewoods Lotteries. This was a vital source of revenue which enabled us to build the research centre and to develop a research programme which achieved international recognition.

Trish Dodd was the prime mover in this, with great support from Phil Rooney and their MD, Jeremy Collis, and we all owe her a huge debt of gratitude. Occasionally individuals with vision, talent and commitment can make a major impact on events and Trish was one of these.

****

On 3 March, Roy was admitted to hospital with a chest infection. He had been feeling weak and unwell and had a temperature. Tom Mangold and the television crew were present when the doctor gave Roy the news and Roy was very frustrated and vented his anger on the tobacco companies whom he blamed for his cancer. "If you brought the bosses of the tobacco companies into this room now, I don't think they would make it to the hospital!"

Within ten days he was at the centre of one of the most emotional events in the whole campaign. He was invited to toss the coin before the start of the derby match between Liverpool and Everton at Anfield on 13 March. It was the last derby match before the famous Kop was to be pulled down and converted to all-seating as a result of the Taylor report into the Hillsborough disaster. The directors and staff of Liverpool Football Club were brilliant in their support and management of the occasion, particularly Brian Hall, an ex-player, who had responsibility for community relations at the club.

Over 44,000 people packed the terraces and stands. Roy's appearance had been well advertised and there was a bucket collection at the gates which raised a record £10,000. He had spent the morning with Ken Dodd and Jean Boht attending the regional conference of Lions Clubs in Crosby and, without a break, he came straight to Anfield where, for two hours, he toured the directors' lounge and every single hospitality box with a big smile and a joke for everyone. He spent seven hours at the ground altogether and spoke to everyone who approached him from the fans to the staff, the stewards and the police. He even did an interview in the Sky Sports studio. He was a sick man but you would never have known it, such was his energy and the force of his personality.

About an hour before kick off he was walking round the perimeter of the ground to get back to the main stand when he was spotted by some fans in the Kop. They must have been keen eyed because he had a woolly cap over his bald head and no distinctive clothing. Some of them chanted his name and he began to smile, at which point he became instantly recognisable to many others. There were about 10,000 fans already in the Kop and, in a marvellous show of affection, they took up the chant and Roy was obviously very moved.

Things quietened down a little as Roy went into the players' tunnel but soon he was leading the players out, wearing the scarves of both Liverpool and Everton. Normally the roar of the crowd on these occasions is deafening but this time it had an extraordinary warmth and the volume was massive and sustained. The chant "There's only one Roy Castle" began to reverberate around the ground and the atmosphere, which was already charged because of the derby match, became electric. The visiting fans at the other end of the ground were also from Liverpool because they were Evertonians and the whole crowd – nearly 45,000 – was on its feet clapping and whistling and chanting, "There's only one Roy Castle". And how right they were! I was in my usual place in the Paddock and found the whole thing very emotional.

As the teams kicked about, Roy walked into the centre circle and saluted the crowd. He waved his scarves and kicked his heels in the air and again the crowd responded with, "There's only one Roy Castle". Roy was experiencing what he richly deserved, the love and respect of the people of Liverpool and he was returning it to them. As I sat incognito in my seat, I felt very happy that something which I had started had created the opportunity for Roy to be recognised in this way before he died.

Chapter 14

Fundraising

During all this excitement there was an enormous amount of work going on in the background. On the fundraising front, individuals and groups of supporters were sending in donations or holding events and their number is too great to mention them all. The Isle of Man and Aughton support groups continued to be very active and new groups were formed. Old friends and colleagues of Roy, led by Derek Hamer, got together in Calderdale, near where Roy was born, and have raised many thousands of pounds to this day, mainly through a Tapathon which they hold every year.

Not surprisingly many of the supporters of the Lung Cancer Fund came from among my patients and their families. Mildred Cooper, whose husband, Barry, died of lung cancer soon after Roy, has been one of the best of these, giving her time and energies freely and enthusiastically and allowing her beautiful home on the Isle of Man to be used for prestige events.

Terry Kavanagh was a patient of mine who had his lung cancer removed about the time when I first set up the charity and, like Roy had never smoked. He was a big admirer of Roy and for nearly ten years has been raising funds with his wife Ann and his many friends, climbing Snowden, running in charity races, holding art auctions and many other activities. Terry is now a trustee of the Foundation and has developed an international profile as a committed advocate for lung cancer patients and the work of the charity.

Bob McAdam was a firefighter in Liverpool and developed lung cancer at the same time as Roy. They met at the Crosby regional convention of the Lions Clubs on the morning of the Derby match at Anfield. Roy spent time with him and promised him that they would open the research centre together when that great day came. Sadly neither of them was to survive that long. However Bob's brother, Peter, and his colleagues in the service have raised huge sums of money for the appeal and his widow Moira has spoken movingly at fundraising events. One of the main rooms in the research centre has been named after Bob McAdam.

David Snowden-Jones, who owns the Cherry Pie Inn near Mold in North Wales, has recently received the MBE for all his efforts on behalf of our appeal and other charities. It pleases me to see people rewarded in this way.

Geoff Knowles would plough a lonely but faithful course in Bolton, raising thousands of pounds by his own initiative and there were many others like him.

Norman Steel was a golfing acquaintance whom I had not seen for a few years. I met him on a plane going to the Isle of Man for one of my clinics and told him what we were trying to do. He agreed to arrange a small dinner for the Fund with some of his business associates. Eight years later he had raised almost £100,000.

Robert Powell came up to Formby to take part in a charity golf day organised by the captain, Tony Lewis. Other golf days raised precious pounds, the most successful of these being held at Huyton and Prescot where David Jones and his friends put on the first of their golf events which, over the years, would go on to raise many thousands of pounds. David now lives in Torquay, where he owns the oldest pub in the town, The Hole in the Wall, a famous watering hole with a unique atmosphere and a brilliant venue for his continued fundraising efforts.

Fundraising, however, was not limited to our traditional areas of support. Roy's profile was beginning to stimulate the nation. His many thousands of long standing and recently acquired admirers sent in donations or organised fundraising events and they were supplemented by thousands more who had, like Roy, been affected by lung cancer and wanted to support him in raising the money to build the world's first lung cancer research centre.

* * * * * * * * * *

At their meeting in May, the trustees approved a business plan prepared by KPMG for the building of the Centre. Brian Case questioned the proposed structure of the charity since he felt that too much was being asked of Sylvia Ingham as Chief Executive and Head of Fundraising but, for the time being, the structure was approved. Meanwhile, it was noted that the management report prepared previously by Touche Ross continued to be implemented.

The trustees were assured that staff expenses were being monitored on a monthly basis and stock and purchasing procedures were in place. A meeting was scheduled with a partner from Touche Ross regarding income and expenditure of events. Sylvia said that there were difficulties caused by the cramped conditions of the office at the hospital but that office procedures would be more easily managed in the new offices to be provided by Littlewoods in August.

At the same meeting the building consultants for the Centre were selected. After tender the following were selected; architects, Franklin Stafford Partnership, quantity surveyors, Everiss Blundell Snowling, mechanical and electrical engineers, Ernest Griffiths, structural engineers, Parkmans. Lace Mawer were appointed as legal advisors to the project.

It was not envisaged that the land would be acquired until the following year when building contractors would be appointed. A commitment to proceed with acquisition of the land and development of the project would depend on raising sufficient money to cover all building and equipment costs as well as putting aside a sizable sum to cover running costs in the early years.

Also at this meeting it was agreed to approach John O'Brien, a senior partner in KPMG, to become a trustee of the Fund and to act as treasurer. John subsequently accepted these roles and served the charity magnificently throughout the period of building and establishment of the Centre as well as the subsequent events. He was treasurer of the charity for seven eventful and highly successful years, finally leaving in 2001 when his job moved to Manchester.

This had been an important trustee meeting and before it was finished we were informed that outline planning permission had been approved for the site. Everything was falling into place. We just needed to be reassured that the money would come in. Over the next few months and even after his death, Roy was to show that we need never have worried.

Chapter 15

Tour of Hope

"He's not going to be on the train - you had better make alternative arrangements!" said Fiona. The Tour of Hope was getting close and Roy had been in hospital for two or three weeks. He was in pain and was unable to swallow solid food because of his cancer.

But Roy was desperate to make the train and asked his consultant if there was any way that he could do it. "Well, we have ways of patching people up to go on a world cruise but I've never heard of anyone wanting to go on a train!" said the doctor. " I don't care if you stuff me, I want to go on that train", said Roy.

And he got his way, though he was desperately ill and only weeks from death.

He was allowed home on Monday, 18 July, physically very low but mentally strong and determined to do whatever he possibly could to raise the money that would build the Centre which would carry his name and be a cause for hope for all those who would develop the disease which was prematurely taking his life away. Later he would say on the train, "I couldn't have ducked this. How could I say I'm not well enough? There must be many people suffering like I am and they're also doing their bit – and so am I."

I met him very early the following morning in the Green Room at GMTV studios in London. He was with Fiona and was about to give the first of dozens of interviews over the next few days. He was pale and thin but his eyes were bright and he was smiling. He must have been feeling dreadful but his professionalism and determination, allied to his bravery and readiness to crack a joke about his condition, were wonderful to behold. The whole nation was to see these qualities displayed in a very public way during the Tour of Hope and an image of Roy Castle would be imprinted on the national consciousness which would continue to generate affection, love and admiration long after he had died. As an example of how to live and die with lung cancer, he was unsurpassed.

Roy was never bitter about his cancer although he had harsh words to say about the tobacco companies. He had a form of lung cancer which is invariably related to smoking but he had never smoked and the only explanation was that he had developed his cancer as a result of singing, dancing and playing his trumpet in smoke filled clubs and theatres. He never asked, "Why me?" Although he didn't want to die, he accepted God's will for him. He had a real living faith and this was a strong motivating force in coping with all the trials and tribulations life was now throwing at him. Fiona was constantly at his side.

From the TV studios we drove to Euston station to take the special train up to Liverpool where the tour would start. At Euston he felt unwell and had to spend an uncomfortable time in the loo. In spite of this he continued to do live radio and television interviews explaining the purpose of the tour and what the Lung Cancer Fund was trying to do. He was barely able to stand long enough to complete a live interview with ITN at midday, but somehow managed it.

We had to wait in a portakabin whilst the train was being prepared but there was a smell of stale smoke inside and Roy had to leave and sit on the platform seat. Eventually he was able to get on the train and lie down in a cabin, which had been specially prepared for him. Once he lay down he didn't move again until the train reached Liverpool. I had arranged for Pauline, our lung cancer nurse in Liverpool, to accompany Roy throughout the tour and she kept going in to check that he was all right. She was not sure he was breathing at one stage and I asked her to be sure that he had not died since he had appeared so ill, but she was able to reassure me.

When we reached Liverpool, there was a large crowd waiting for him as well as television, press and radio. Roy got out of his cabin and appeared at the door of the carriage with a beaming smile on his face and was greeted enthusiastically. The people of Liverpool have a very big heart and they had adopted Roy as one of their own. They recognised his courage and good humour in the face of adversity and they loved him for it. They welcomed him back to Liverpool for the last time and clearly showed their affection and admiration for him. In Liverpool they know all about lung cancer and Roy was doing something extraordinary for them, giving them pride that the world's only lung cancer research centre was to be built in their city and giving them hope that this dreadful disease, which had affected so many of them, would one day be conquered.

From Lime Street station Roy was driven to the Moat House hotel to rest before the show, which had been arranged at the Empire that evening. 'For the Love of Roy' had been put together by Norman and

Cheryl Williams and their friends and would prove to be one of the most emotionally charged evenings ever seen at this famous theatre. I was unable to attend, which saddened me greatly at the time and has done so ever since. I was due to receive an Honorary Fellowship from John Moores University the following day and Elizabeth and I had to attend a Graduation Dinner on the same night as the show.

The Empire was packed, tickets having sold out in two hours. The air of expectancy and emotion was tangible and everyone wondered what part Roy could possibly play, knowing that he was so desperately ill. The show was produced by Johnnie Hamp and provided great entertainment. Cliff Richard topped the bill with contributions from Sir John Mills, Vince Earl, Joe Brown, The Drifters, Buck's Fizz, the Merseybeats, Sean Styles, Kenny Ball, Mike McCartney and Gerry Marsden.

At the end of the show Roy had still not appeared. Gerry Marsden began to sing, *You'll Never Walk Alone* and the whole audience was up on its feet joining in, hands in the air and entwined. This went on for a long time and many people were crying. At the end Roy came on to the stage, thin and pale and weak. Sir John Mills said afterwards that he did not know how Roy had managed it. He had seen him sitting in the wings and did not believe he would have the strength to make it.

The clapping and cheering were deafening and went on and on. Eventually it died down and everyone waited for Roy to speak. The atmosphere was electric and Roy was visibly moved, wiping a tear from his eye. Then, in a way that only Roy could do, he made a joke about himself and brought everyone back down to earth. "What a way to resurrect a career!" he said. He brought the house down and that was the last time that Roy ever appeared on stage.

＊＊＊＊＊＊＊＊＊＊＊＊＊

The next morning, Wednesday, 20 July, Lime Street station was full of people, colour, banners and noise. A band was playing and children were dancing. The media were out in strength for the start of the Tour of Hope which would take the special train through twelve major cities and over 1,600 miles in the next three days. Massive media coverage would make it an event that would remain in the memories of many thousands of people all over the country for many years to come.

The only problem was that on this day there was a national train strike! Strenuous efforts had been made with the rail union to get a special dispensation for the first day of the Tour of Hope but without success. Arthur Johnson, however, used his contacts at Liverpool Football Club and arranged to borrow their first team coach for the first leg of the journey.

Speeches were made by myself and Harry Rimmer, Leader of Liverpool City Council, who announced that the proposed site of the research centre would be donated to the Lung Cancer Fund by the city. When Roy got up to speak, Fiona indicated to me to support him from behind since she was afraid that he was so weak that he might fall over. Roy spotted a small child at the back of the crowd and told everyone that what we were doing was for our children and our children's children.

I was unable to go on the tour because of my work and said goodbye to Roy on the coach. I wondered if I would see him again because he was clearly very ill and I spent a few private moments with him. The coach pulled out of the station with Roy's pale face smiling through the window. He would not return to Liverpool.

* * * * * * * * * * * *

Manchester Arndale Centre was the first stop but Roy was too ill to get off and Fiona went in with Simon Bates, a well known Radio 1 DJ. On then to Huddersfield and Roy was woken by Fiona to look at the Yorkshire moors for the last time. "I used to go fishing and ride my bike down there," he said. In the market square, where everyone could see him, he was given a microphone and spoke to the crowd. He seemed energised by being in his native Yorkshire and near his home town. Children from the primary school in Scholes, where Roy was born, came out to sing to him.

The long journey continued up to Newcastle where they arrived late in the evening. The police sent an outrider to meet the coach and hurry its progress through the heavy traffic. Roy was very excited and when the cast of *Byker Grove* came on the bus, there was a lot of hugging and crying. "Hey, I'm the one who's ill!" he said.

Despite the fact that he had been physically sick, he wanted to get off the bus and speak to the people. Little children in pink tutus sang and danced for him and he cried. The children cried also and he told them, "I don't want anyone to become like me. Please don't smoke."

Because of his weakness the plans were changed and Roy was flown straight to Glasgow in Littlewoods' private plane instead of going by bus. Sylvia Ingham told me that Fiona thought he would die that night. Several times during the tour Fiona asked him if he would like to call a halt and go back home but each time he refused. There were times also when he would do without his morphine, which he took for pain control, so that he would be clear-headed to meet the crowds and do his media interviews. His courage was astonishing.

Next morning, at Glasgow Central station, he was much brighter as he laughed and joked with the crowd. At one stage he put on the Piper's hat and there was more singing, dancing and television cameras. Before the end of the tour there would be 119 television slots, 153 radio slots and extensive national and regional press coverage of the tour and its purpose. Sylvia and her team had done an exceptional job.

As the train rattled down to Carlisle, Roy felt much worse and began to have headaches. Sylvia rang me in Liverpool and I advised her to get a specialist to see him when they reached Carlisle. The oncologist came on to the train and was able to reassure Roy that all of his symptoms were to be expected and were normal for someone in his condition. "Let's get on, then," he said. He then went to the city centre where CFM Radio put on a large roadshow with hundreds of people cheering and clapping. Roy received the same affectionate and enthusiastic reception wherever he went and I have often felt happy to have been instrumental, through the charity which I had founded, in creating the opportunity for him to see clearly, before the end of his life, how much he was loved and admired by so many people.

And so the tour continued at breakneck speed through Birmingham, Cardiff, Bristol, Plymouth and Brighton. The crowds and the cameras came out to see them wherever they went and all the time money was being donated and pledged for the research centre in Liverpool.

****

The train pulled into Waterloo International station after three action packed days. It was the first passenger train ever to arrive at the station and there was a mass of admirers and celebrities to meet Roy and Fiona. After getting off the train, they pushed Roy in his wheelchair up to the engine where they unveiled the nameplate which read, 'Roy Castle OBE'. Roy had no idea that the train which had carried him all round the country was, in fact, called after him and he was very excited and proud.

They then travelled by car with a police escort to the hotel where an end of tour reception was planned. As they drove down the Mall in front of Buckingham Palace, Roy asked, "Have you arranged something else?" "I wish", replied Sylvia.

At the reception it was announced that £1.3million, including a gift from Diana, Princess of Wales, had been donated or pledged in just three days, a phenomenal achievement. Several of us made speeches, including Robert Powell, who arrived full of enthusiasm but hot and sweaty, having mistakenly gone to another hotel of the same name in a different part of London. Last of all Roy got up to speak and it was difficult to hold back the emotion. Here was a sick and dying man who could barely stand, who had just travelled around the country on an uncomfortable train for three days, who stood to gain nothing from what he had done but who was determined to do "his bit" for others. In a weak but clear voice, with his hand on his chest, he said, "Everything has been said – except from my heart and my heart says everything. Thank you so much."

These were his last public words and, as he left the hotel in his wheelchair, I said goodbye to him with a heavy heart.

Chapter 16

'No Tears, Just Lots of Joy'

Roy was taken home by Fiona and made no more public appearances or statements. He had given his all and would spend his last few weeks in privacy. He worked at completing his autobiography, writing out in longhand the final chapters, knowing full well that the story would soon be over.

I asked Fiona if I could visit him but she preferred that I didn't. Sylvia went to see him and he made her promise to continue the work. It wasn't clear how long Roy had left and she went off to Florida with her family for a much-deserved holiday.

While she was away I got a call from a family friend to tell me that her father, Ray Wanless, had taken ill and was in hospital in Darlington. It was twelve months since I had operated on him for lung cancer and he had particularly enjoyed the extra time with his grandchildren but it seemed that the disease had returned. I arranged his transfer to Liverpool to be under my care again and contacted Sylvia who returned from holiday to be with him.

It transpired therefore that, at the same time as Roy was dying, Sylvia's father was also nearing the end of his life. It was unsure who would die first and Sylvia and Fiona would talk to each other regularly, giving each other what support they could. Just a few days before Sylvia's father died, Fiona sent her an arrangement of flowers with the message "We love you very much and we are thinking about you". They had formed a close friendship already but this period of mutual suffering and support appeared to bring them even closer together.

Ray Wanless died peacefully in the Cardiothoracic Centre where the Lung Cancer Fund had been born four and a half years previously. In the days before the funeral, Roy's condition worsened and Fiona rang me for help and reassurance as Roy struggled for breath. I was later told that she said, "I want to bring the TV cameras in now and see how their hero is dying". Only those who have experienced it know how distressing it is to feel completely helpless as a loved one goes through the agonies of death. I was able to comfort her a little by saying that Roy was well sedated and that he was not conscious of what was going on; that, in fact, at that moment, she was suffering much more than him. She said afterwards that she chose to believe me and that this helped.

As we drove up to Cumbria for the funeral of Sylvia's father, we knew that Roy was close to death. As a surgeon who was never off duty, I always carried a long-range bleep - it was before the days of the mobile phones – and I had arranged for my daughter Catherine to contact me as soon as word reached the office in Liverpool. It had been decided not to tell Sylvia until after her father's funeral but a press release had been prepared and media interviews would be required.

I waited outside the church for as long as possible but eventually had to go inside. I silenced my bleep and put it on vibration. Sylvia had asked me to read the lesson and I went to the lectern at the appropriate moment. Halfway through the text I felt the bleep buzzing in my pocket and this is how I knew that Roy had died. It was an emotional moment and I suppose it was my surgical training which helped me to continue reading without interruption. The date was 2 September 1994 and 'Duracell man' had finally stopped running.

At the end of the service, outside the church, I authorised the release of the press statement and did some hurried interviews over the telephone, the first one with Roger Phillips of Radio Merseyside, which was only right in view of the bond which had developed between Roy and the people of Liverpool.

Roy's death was headline news on all the television and radio channels. A greatly loved and admired Christian gentleman had passed away and there was national sorrow. Fiona made her famous "No flowers, no tears, just lots of joy" interview. Many people tried to express what Roy had meant to them.

Later that night, on live television, Robert Powell described how his breath had been taken away by watching the public response to Roy during the last few months of his illness and he recalled how, at a lunch earlier in the year with directors of Littlewoods, which Roy had interrupted his treatment to attend, Roy had been so funny that they had all been crying with laughter. I thought that these two examples of Roy's character and personality made a good start at summing up the effect that Roy had on people and the type of man he was. More considered tributes would follow later.

****

"I've seen you on television!" Amazingly, these were the first words that Cliff Richard ever spoke to me. I had been a fan since 1958 and he greeted me with these words as I walked across to him in Fiona's house before the Service of Thanksgiving at Gold Hill Baptist church. It was 8 September and Roy had been cremated at a private family service earlier in the day.

Cliff, later to be knighted, had become a close friend of Roy and Fiona and would, on many occasions, express his deep admiration and affection for them. He would talk about the way Roy "had died in public" giving a truly wonderful example of how to cope with cancer and how to die with faith and courage. Cliff's support for the Appeal meant a great deal to everyone involved and his generosity and loyalty over the years has been an important ingredient in its success.

The service was led by the Pastor, Rev Jim Graham, and Roy's children, Julia, Antonia and Ben all contributed, as did Birthe, the wife of their eldest son Daniel. Sir Harry Secombe spoke movingly about Roy and Cliff sang unaccompanied. I gave my own tribute to Roy.

We all dispersed not knowing what the future would bring but determined to keep Roy's memory alive and complete the task to which he had given the last eight months of his life.

✳✳✳✳✳✳✳✳✳✳✳✳✳✳

A second Thanksgiving Service was held in London at All Souls Church, Langham Place next to Broadcasting House. The Chairman of Governors of the BBC and other dignitaries attended together with Roy's colleagues and friends from showbusiness. Tributes were made by Norris McWhirter, Roy's co-presenter of Record Breakers for many years, Don Maclean and Cliff Richard. Cliff also sang and Ben Castle played his saxophone. Perhaps most moving of all was the playing of a record made by Roy shortly before his death. "I am a New Creation" brought tears to the eyes as Roy's voice penetrated hearts and minds and we felt reassured that he had gone to a better place.

The service had been recorded by BBC radio and, as we drove back to Liverpool, we listened and once again experienced the emotions of the occasion. The whole service was broadcast with the exception of my own tribute to Roy.

✳✳✳✳✳✳✳✳✳✳✳✳✳✳

On 20 October, a Celebration in Memory of Roy Castle was held in the Cathedral of Christ the King in Liverpool. All week I had presented Thought for the Day on BBC Radio Merseyside, highlighting different aspects of Roy's personality, character and faith and how these were revealed in the way he had dealt with his cancer and approaching death. There are some people, I said, who light up the ways of the world with their faith and their love, and such a man was Roy Castle.

The service was led by Archbishop Derek Worlock together with Rev Keith Hobbs, General Superintendent of the Lancashire and Cheshire Association of Baptist Churches. It was a Thursday afternoon but the cathedral was packed to overflowing and the service was broadcast live by Radio Merseyside.

City and University dignitaries attended along with many celebrities including Ken Dodd, Gerry Marsden and Faith Brown. Rick Wakeman had composed and played a special piece for the service.

Tributes were made by Daniel Castle, who described how his father always gave himself right to the end and was never resentful or bitter but grateful to God for the life he had had. John Griffith, Editor of the Liverpool Echo, spoke eloquently of Roy's example and dedication and Jean Boht brought a worried frown to the Archbishop's face when she had everyone tap dancing in their seats. Readings were given by Richard Madeley and Judy Finnegan. Derek Worlock spoke of his own admiration for Roy, describing him as a man of mountainous courage and humble resilience adding his appreciation of the work of the Lung Cancer Fund of which he had been Vice President since his operation for lung cancer two years previously.

The service closed with a loud and emotional singing of "You'll never walk alone" and Fiona, in her own words, sang her socks off.

Chapter 17

Fag Ends

During all this time of making plans for a research centre and raising the necessary funds to build it, the essential work of the charity continued to develop and expand. John Field's research was beginning to attract international attention and, in July 1994 when publicity for the Tour of Hope was at its height, we arranged, in the University of Liverpool, the first of an annual series of workshops for scientists from academic centres around the world who were interested in the early detection of lung cancer.

From this group of distinguished scientists we formed an Advisory Panel to monitor and evaluate our research programme and to collaborate with it. I was thrilled that internationally respected scientists like Dr Jim Mulshine, Head of Biomarkers at the National Cancer Institute in Washington, and Professor Mel Tockman from the Johns Hopkins University in Baltimore, were prepared to take time out from their very heavy schedules to come to Liverpool each year and take such an interest in our work.

The reason, of course, was that they could see the commitment we had made to study a much neglected cancer and the opportunity that we had, because of the extent of the disease in Liverpool, to make a major contribution to the worldwide effort to defeat lung cancer. They could see that we were already providing leadership and Professor Tockman went on to BBC television and described the importance of our work by explaining that it was as if the scientists on the Advisory Panel were each, in their own laboratory, building their own beautiful motor car but that it was the Lung Cancer Fund which was building the super highway on which we could all drive our cars together to achieve our common goal of defeating lung cancer. This was quite a tribute for a fledgling organisation.

****

It was also during this year that I first came across Fag Ends, a group of young people led by Melody McGrillis, who had given up smoking and were trying to do something to help other people quit in one of the poorer areas of Liverpool. They had the idea of working, within their own communities, with their peers on a voluntary basis and in a completely non-judgemental way. Their approach was more grass roots and very different from that normally taken by seasoned health professionals and it appealed to me.

Mel and her friends had persuaded their GP to let them have a desk and a telephone once a week and their enthusiasm was infectious. I decided to help them and, over the next few years, gave them a series of small grants, firstly to buy a computer, then to rent an office space and finally to employ some staff. Fag Ends went from strength to strength and we eventually absorbed them into the Foundation, becoming Roy Castle Fag Ends. They would subsequently expand and provide for the NHS a service right across Merseyside and achieve success rates way above the standard set by the Department of Health. They have never lost their fundamental ethos and their achievements have been truly great.

It was at about this time also that I was first approached by Professor Jane Springett and Dr Lesley Dugdill of Liverpool John Moores University with a proposal to study the attitudes and perceptions of young people with regard to smoking. Their plan was to study children from nine to thirteen years of age but I suggested that they should look at children between six and nine. My thinking was to try to understand what children of this age were thinking before they began to smoke, in the hope of being able to develop programmes in primary schools which would prevent children ever starting to smoke.

On this basis we gave them a grant and they have since conducted a unique and immensely important research programme following a group of more than two hundred children from the age of five until they are now in secondary school where some are already experimenting with smoking. Much of the early work was done by Lorna Porcellato, a Canadian teacher, whose enthusiasm and ability to relate to children ensured the success of the project in its first defining years.

The work has become more complex with the scattering of the children to a number of secondary schools but it is continuing and will do so at least until they leave school. This will provide a unique cohort of children and young adults whose perceptions and habits of smoking will have been monitored from a very young age. Teaching materials, based on this research, have already been produced and are available to primary schools all over the country.

I was very keen for us to expand our work with children and was delighted when we received an application for funding from two

Merseyside teachers, Sue Occleston and Anne Case, for a smoking prevention project in primary schools in Knowsley. This was based on the Child to Child programme which had been developed in France for a variety of health topics. The aim was to enhance the self-esteem of the children taking part and to enable them to make their own choices about smoking rather than being led into it by their peers or other influences.

We ran this programme in several schools in Knowsley and it was so well received by the children, their parents and teachers that we ran another the following year in an adjoining district, this time with the help of European funding.

We also brought a specialist over from Canada to run a training course in smoking cessation among low income women in Liverpool. The underlying principle of this was again to enhance their self esteem and help them to take charge of their own lives and make their own lifestyle decisions.

* * * * * * * * * * *

I had always envisaged the charity as a provider of grants to other universities outside Liverpool, on the basis that lung cancer was a national problem and that the chances of success against it were better if a collaborative effort could be made by scientists in different universities with different skills and experience. This was good in theory but quite ambitious in the light of how small we still were and, in retrospect, impracticable considering how much money would be needed to build and run the research centre in Liverpool.

However, at this time, I still saw the charity as leading the way in lung cancer research in the UK, since no one else seemed to have much interest and I hoped that the Roy Castle Centre would become the hub for a co-ordinated national scientific research programme into lung cancer. In view of this, we agreed to provide a shared grant to the universities of Manchester and Dundee to look at the role of angiogenesis in tumour growth and metastasis in lung cancer in the elderly. The application had been properly peer reviewed by external referees and the programme ran for three years.

Meanwhile the Lung Cancer Fund continued to build on Roy's legacy. 'King Courage' was how the *Liverpool Daily Post* had described him the day after he died and we would have to draw on this inspiration again and again as we faced the immense task ahead of us.

Chapter 18

Personality of the Year

The Board of Trustees met on 1 August, just a month before Roy died, for some important decisions. Stephen Quicke, who would design and oversee the building of the research centre, presented several ideas for the external appearance of the building which varied from the functional to the futuristic.

In view of the international and unique nature of the project, it was felt important that the Centre should have a distinct and memorable appearance that would be recognised around the world of lung cancer research. Indeed, after it had been completed, it did one day appear on the cover of an international cancer journal. The design would also, we hoped, keep it in the public eye and continue to draw funds for the important work going on inside.

The present, instantly recognisable design, or Option A, as it was then, was adopted and the design team authorised to proceed with drawings for detailed planning application to Liverpool City Council. Another advantage of Option A was that it was designed to allow the easy incorporation of a second phase in the future over the proposed car park.

The cost was estimated at £2.3million plus a further £1million for fitting out and equipment. At that time we had £648,000 in the bank and more was arriving every day. It was agreed, with the consultants, however, that no fees would be charged if, by any chance, the project did not proceed. We hoped to be in a position to go to tender in January 1995.

A decision was made to apply for Objective One funding, with millions of pounds of European money coming into Merseyside for regeneration. Geoffrey Piper suggested that National Lottery funding might be available through the Millennium Commission. Much time, effort and money would be spent on these over the next few years but we were never successful, something which remains a mystery to many people to this day.

At the same meeting, Sylvia reported on the extraordinary success of the Tour of Hope, with 1,600 miles covered, 119 television and 153 radio slots and extensive coverage in the national and regional press. A letter had been received from the Queen, as well as a note from Princess Diana, together with a generous donation.

She also indicated that she was preparing plans for fourteen regional fundraising offices around the UK. We would eventually only open up in Glasgow, London, Cumbria and Newcastle over the next few years but she was never able to make a success of these and all would close down except for Glasgow, which only just survived because we were developing the headquarters of our patient care activities there under the guidance of some exceptional people.

The Littlewoods Organisation continued to give us massive support and the fundraising team had recently moved into rent free accommodation in their head office in Old Hall Street, Liverpool. This meant leaving the Cardiothoracic Centre where the Lung Cancer Fund had been born but it was the right decision and would allow the team to expand to match the astonishing growth of the charity.

At this same meeting, the Trustees established a remuneration committee to review Sylvia's whole employment package and those of our other employees. Terms of reference were also agreed for the Executive Group, chaired by Sylvia as Chief Executive, enabling it to implement the policies and decisions of the Board, to manage budgets agreed by the Board and instructing them to keep the Board fully informed on all financial and other matters relevant to the activities of the Fund.

* * * * * * * * * * *

As light relief from all this serious activity, we were back at the House of Lords on 9 September. Geraldine Jamieson, a leading broadcaster on the Isle of Man, had become a staunch friend and supporter of the Lung Cancer Fund. Drawing on the many friends in showbusiness and public life whom she had made through her work, she organised a magical evening in the Cholmondely Room. She persuaded Michael Dobbs, well known as author of *House of Cards*, to be the main speaker and the evening was hosted by Major Peter Horsfall, Staff Superintendent at the House of Lords, who would also become a firm friend and supporter.

Significantly that evening, Sylvia Ingham had persuaded Coca Cola to take a table and senior managers of this major company would lend important support to the charity for years to come.

Other speakers were Professor Peter Toyne, Vice Chancellor of John Moores University and myself. I had never envisaged that I would one day make a speech in the House of Lords!

****

Another Trustees' meeting took place on 17 October. The Remuneration Committee had met and were embarking on a review of the appraisal and counselling procedures for the Chief Executive.

By now we had £1.65million in the bank and it was anticipated that this would rise to £2.5million by the end of the year. Littlewoods had confirmed their support for at least another two years and scratchcard income from this source would be huge.

On this basis, the Trustees agreed to go to tender in January, after planning approval had been obtained. Negotiations were in the final stages for acquisition of the land from the City Council at no net cost to the Fund and the application for Objective One funding was almost completed, discussions having taken place with the Government Office on Merseyside. Terms of contract with the professionals involved in building the Centre were close to being settled. We were seriously on the move.

****

Through all this we had not forgotten Roy, and with great energy Fiona was doing everything asked of her to promote the Lung Cancer Fund. Towards the end of the year the *Today* programme on BBC Radio 4 began their annual listener vote for Personality of the Year.

The main candidates to emerge were Nelson Mandela, Tony Blair, John Major and Roy Castle. Roy, who was such a straightforward and humble person, would have been amazed to have found himself in such company but the rest of us thought it completely appropriate.

Fiona was invited into the studio very early one dark morning at the end of December to hear the result announced live on the programme. I don't think she expected Roy to win this particular award because of the strength of the other candidates and since many of the listeners were perhaps not Roy's natural audience. In fact, Roy came top of the poll and was declared Radio 4 Personality of the Year.

How could it ever have been anyone else?

Chapter 19

New Name – Same Mission

Barry Cooper had died in November 1994 and early in 1995 we lost Eric Morris. I was very saddened to lose two patients of whom I had become very fond and who had helped me in different but significant ways. Barry's widow, Mildred, has continued to be a staunch friend and supporter and Eric had been with me from the very beginning, one of those who had sat with me at the very first meeting in my office in April 1990 and helped me set up the Lung Cancer Fund. Both of them are remembered in the Roy Castle Centre but that is only a small acknowledgement for the important parts they played in the development of an ambitious idea. May they rest in peace.

January 1995 saw me flying off again to Malaysia to operate and to teach. I often travelled at this stage and grasped every opportunity to tell everyone I met about the work in Liverpool. I still had a busy surgical practice at home and held senior Board responsibilities at the Cardiothoracic Centre as Director of Education and Research. I chaired a Medical Research Council Working Party on Cancer of the Oesophagus and attended many scientific meetings. Young surgeons continued to arrive from the USA and other countries for training in thoracic surgery so that, all in all, it was a very busy time. I often visited the United States for conferences, or to advise manufacturers on the development of instruments for keyhole surgery in the chest.

And all the while the Lung Cancer Fund was expanding quickly and making important decisions. Fortunately, I was surrounded in every area by committed, talented people who bore much of the strain.

At their January meeting the Trustees were given legal advice about their liability, now that large sums of money were being accrued and a major capital project was being planned. We were advised that the legal status of the charity needed to be changed and that this would best be done by the winding up of the present charity and the transfer of all assets and liabilities to a new charitable company, limited by guarantee. The Charity Commission had indicated that it was willing to expedite the legal change. This should be done before any contracts were signed for the new research centre.

In March, I was delighted to receive a Special Award from the Duke of Westminster at the North West Business Awards and, in April, Roy was posthumously given the Freedom of the City of Liverpool. This meant another speech but it was never difficult to talk about Roy and pay tribute to him. This great honour, announced a day or two before his death, was richly deserved and his scroll still hangs in the Roy Castle Centre. To complement this, Fiona received an Honorary Degree from the University of Liverpool at their Graduation Ceremony in July.

On 26 April, the trustees met and were notified that the constitution for the new charity had been agreed with the Charity Commission and was now in a form that was ready to be signed and sent to Companies House to be registered there, following which it would be forwarded to the Charity Commission. The Lung Cancer Fund could not be wound up until the new company had been registered and the transfer of assets and liabilities did not come into effect until 1 July 1995, when the entire charitable operations previously carried out by the Lung Cancer Fund were transferred to the newly named Roy Castle Cause for Hope Foundation (The Lung Cancer Fund), a charitable company limited by guarantee. The Lung Cancer Fund was finally wound up on 1 August 1995.

I wrote to Fiona inviting her to become a Trustee of the new organisation but she declined, saying that she was not a "committee person" and that she could contribute more effectively in her current role. The remainder of the Trustees transferred to the new charity, as did the Chief Executive and all her staff. The mission and purpose remained unchanged so that the charity remained exactly the same except for a new name and legal status.

There had been much debate about the name and not all were in favour of including Roy's name. I strongly argued for it in recognition of what Roy had done for us and so that this should never be forgotten. It was also very clear that his name would continue to help us achieve our aims. We finally settled on a compromise title, The Roy Castle Cause for Hope Foundation (The Lung Cancer Fund), which was a bit of a mouthful and did not indicate which disease we were targeting. It was later changed to The Roy Castle Lung Cancer Foundation and has remained unaltered since then. Fiona was, of course, consulted at each step and readily gave her agreement.

About this time Lady Pilkington's health began to deteriorate. She had been one of my most ardent supporters, never missed a function (and organised many of her own) and helped us financially time after time. It was becoming progressively more difficult for her to be actively involved. Mavis had given us outstanding support and I had always been able to turn to her when I need funds for some special event or other purpose. People like her are few and far between and I grew very fond of her. She agreed to take the nomination of Life President but her failing health prevented her doing much more for us, although she remained a firm friend.

Her position as President was taken by John Moores who had been so influential in acquiring for us, and maintaining, the support of the Littlewoods Organisation, a relationship which, over several years, brought millions of pounds into the charity.

In June, we had the second meeting of our International Scientific Advisory Panel to review our research plans and to advise on the design of the research centre. Their visit was combined with a workshop on early detection of lung cancer, attended by leading scientists in the field from Europe and North America. This was an expensive exercise but, in my view, essential if we were to ensure the scientific validity and appropriateness of our research proposals and our concepts for the building.

This panel was to continue to meet at regular intervals over the next few years and their input and support was greatly reassuring to me and to the Trustees, since none of us was a cancer scientist, but held the firm view that early detection was the future so far as lung cancer management was concerned. Research into new treatments of established disease was good and necessary but the disease had to be detected at an earlier stage, before any shadow appeared on the lungs, when the genetic process leading up to clinical disease was still incomplete. Non toxic agents could then be developed to arrest this process and prevent lung cancer progressing to the stage where a tumour developed. This method of management, known as chemoprevention, is already in use in some other cancers, most notably breast cancer.

The speed of growth of the charity was astounding. We had exploded on to the scene, brought in huge sums of money and were already making an international impact. The speed of our progress would result in some problems later but would also give us the opportunity to achieve what had never been done before, a major lung cancer research programme, a much better deal for lung cancer patients and their families and massively increased awareness of the reality of passive smoking.

Chapter 20

Ups and Downs

We were still only half way through 1995. To keep me sane I still found time to play golf and my friend David Appleton, who was Captain at Formby that year, arranged a golf day for the Foundation which was a financial success because of the enthusiasm of the members and because expenses were kept to a minimum. The same applied to the Isle of Man and Huyton and Prescot. The Trustees, however, expressed some concern at the poor return for the time and energy expended at some of the golf days arranged at that time by the Foundation. The problem appeared to be due to the involvement of too many celebrities and the use of professional organisers.

Effective fundraising continued in many other ways up and down the country. In June, Peter McAdam, with the full support of his Chief Fire Officer on Merseyside, Andrew Best, organised a 'Trailblazers' tour of the UK with several of his colleagues in a red fire engine, calling at local fire stations and challenging the local fire-fighters to an 'Everest Climb'. They would park the vehicle in a prominent location and count the time it took a team from either side to climb to the top of the ladder and back down again. Crowds of people came to watch and the collection buckets were full.

****

Every year, at the beginning of July, the Isle of Man Parliament, which has been in existence for over a thousand years, holds a ceremony, full of pageant, on Tynwald Hill, the site of the original parliament, at which all the Bills passed through the Parliament that year are promulgated. The Queen, or a member of the Royal Family, frequently presides. The stands are full and the occasion is hugely popular. This year, accompanied by Elizabeth, I was very privileged to be one of three guests of honour. After an evening reception and Beat the Retreat at Government House, we were taken the following day on a tour of the island and places of interest. The Tynwald ceremony was spectacular and afterwards there was a garden party at Government House and a banquet in the evening. This was for me a culmination of eighteen years of service as a thoracic surgeon to the people of the Isle of Man.

A couple of days after this we were down in London for the launch of the charity as a Foundation attended by many celebrities, including Sir Harry Secombe, Sir John Mills. Cilla Black, Gloria Hunniford, Frank Bruno, Robert Powell and Faith Brown. Then, from 20 to 23 July the second Tour of Hope around the UK took place. Starting at Liverpool and led on this occasion by Fiona, the tour took in Blackpool, Carlisle, Edinburgh, Newcastle, York, Derby, Cardiff, Bristol, Bournemouth and Brighton, finishing at Victoria station. That night a show was put on at the Palladium with Cliff Richard, Jimmy Tarbuck, Joe Brown and many others. The tour was another great success, sponsored once more by Littlewoods, and raising large sums of money everywhere. The media exposure was massive and by this time there were very few people in the country who had not heard of the Roy Castle Foundation and its ambition to build in Liverpool the world's first lung cancer research centre.

* * * * * * * * * * * * *

I was very upset during the summer when my daughter, Catherine, left the charity. She had been with us for four years and had done an outstanding job to the extent that, to this day, people still remember her and ask after her. She was becoming increasingly unhappy in her relationship with Sylvia Ingham, who eventually decided she no longer required a Personal Assistant and proposed that Catherine should be made redundant. The Executive had no choice but to go along with this. It was a deeply unhappy experience for me and my family which only patience and prayer were able eventually to resolve.

* * * * * * * * * * * * *

In August, we achieved another first. The Trustees agreed fifty per cent funding for the appointment of a Smoking Prevention Co-ordinator for the City of Liverpool, the first of its kind in the country. I had proposed this idea to Glyn Thomson, Head of Environmental Health at the City Council, and it was a further development of the ongoing relationship which I had developed with the Council on smoking issues. The speech which I had made to the full City Council in December 1991 had resulted, in 1992, in the establishment of a Tobacco Abuse Working Party, on which I served, and this had produced a City Strategy on tobacco abuse.

It appeared obvious to me that Liverpool, where one in five of its citizens died of a smoking related disease, should have someone wholly dedicated to addressing all matters related to tobacco consumption in the city and to co-ordinate efforts to reduce the heavy toll which both active and passive smoking were causing. Christine Owens was appointed to the post and one of her tasks was to campaign for smoke free areas in public places. The Leader of the City Council at the time, Harry Rimmer, said, "This project will sow the seeds for future generations of Liverpool citizens to enjoy a better standard of health." How right he was, although the effect of this appointment was to extend far beyond the boundaries of Liverpool.

* * * * * * * * * * * * *

For several months I had been working on a book about Roy and this was published in September. Entitled *Roy Castle Remembered*, it was a collection of anecdotes and memories of Roy from family, friends, fans and colleagues. I made a national appeal for stories about Roy and was inundated with material from all kinds of people, including many who had only met him once many years before but on whom he had made an impression which they had never forgotten. The same message came through again and again, of a warm, cheerful, sympathetic man with great powers of communication and whose personality made an instant impact giving people a real feel good factor. The book was my personal tribute to Roy.

* * * * * * * * * * * * *

All year we had been waiting for a decision on our application for European funding. Merseyside had been declared an Objective One area as one of the poorest regions in Europe and in need of massive investment for regeneration. There were several criteria for eligibility and we felt that we met most of these. We believed that real economic benefits would result from building the research centre, including job creation, training, business opportunities, regeneration of derelict land, development of leading edge technologies and the enhancement of the image of Merseyside worldwide.

We had been promised a decision in May but this was delayed until July and finally in October we were informed that our application was unsuccessful, since it involved medical research and did not fit clearly into any single individual criteria but was spread across them all. We could not understand why we had not been told this at the beginning, before spending large amounts of money on preparing our application, especially as we had been asked in May to update our application for further consideration by the Technical Panel.

The public outcry was huge with headlines about faceless Eurocrats and other severe criticisms in the local press. People were bewildered and angry and our office was besieged with callers saying, "Don't worry, we'll get the money for you". The consequence of the failure to secure this funding was that we would have to use money set aside for research. It was a great disappointment to me and to everyone connected with the Foundation but we were determined to press ahead, even though it looked as if the project, which was addressing one of the major public health problems affecting the nation, would not be able to rely on any significant public funding.

****

The governor of the Isle of Man, Sir Lawrence Jones, died suddenly on Sunday, 23 September 1995. He had come under my care shortly beforehand, having coughed up some blood. I had diagnosed small cell lung cancer and the plan was to treat him with chemotherapy. He was due to leave the island on completion of his term of office on Monday, 25th and the committee of the Lung Cancer Fund on the island had a very pleasant lunch with him at Government House on Friday 21st. There had been no inkling that anything untoward could happen since he appeared very well and in good form. The timing of his death was extraordinary and the whole Island was deeply shocked. His funeral took place the following Friday and Elizabeth and I were privileged to be invited to attend.

****

Also in September, tender documents to build the research centre were issued to four companies. At their November meeting, John O'Brien informed the Trustees that a bid for National Lottery funding had now been submitted but, irrespective of whether this was successful or not, his view was that, following an analysis of income and expenditure for 1995, together with budget forecasts for 1995, 96 and 97 and a prudent estimate of grant expenditure, he could recommend to the Trustees that building work could now begin. This was music to my ears and was approved unanimously by the Trustees. The total cost of building fitting out the Centre, including fees and contingency, would be £3,850,000.

At the same meeting in November, the employment issues relating to my daughter, Catherine, leaving the charity were resolved. I offered my resignation as Chairman because of the conflict of interest which had arisen in a potentially damaging matter for the Foundation involving my own family. The unanimous view of the Trustees was that they had full confidence in me and my resignation would be inappropriate.

In December, the bid from Moss Construction to build the Centre was accepted but contracts could not be signed until the Development Agreement and Lease acquiring the land from the City Council had been signed. To me, this seemed to take forever and I became very frustrated with our lawyers for their apparent slowness in dealing with the matter. I was naturally impatient to start building as soon as possible. In fact, it was only a matter of weeks away.

Chapter 21

An Historic Day

We started 1996 with Fag Ends opening up the first ever telephone helpline in Liverpool for people wanting to give up smoking. January is a time when many smokers decide to give up and, not surprisingly, the helpline was busy. To me it was remarkable that something similar had never been done before.

At this time, also, Irene Trevorrow joined the charity with her friend Cath Steele and both proved to be very willing, loyal and effective workers for the charity over a long period of time. Their job was to develop payroll giving, whereby anyone in employment could arrange to have a small sum deducted from their salary and passed directly to the Foundation as a donation. This was the beginnings of an effort to get away from relying entirely on the unpredictable success of events and their associated publicity to raise funds. It would be several more years before we got this right.

The agreement with the City Council releasing the land to us was finally signed on 26 January 1996 and, on 11 February, the Letter of Intent, committing us to the construction of the research centre, was signed and sent off to the builders. Moss Construction were allowed on site on 19 February when National Car Parks moved out, the site having been derelict since 1941 when a land mine had destroyed the buildings on it.

On 26 February, work formally began to build the Roy Castle International Centre for Lung Cancer Research. It was a momentous and historic day, the culmination of years of dreams and hard work, but yet it was only the start of a journey which we believed would one day make a major contribution to the eventual elimination of lung cancer and all the devastation which it could cause. We were realistic and knew that many dangers and difficulties might lie ahead, although it must be said that we did not appreciate the intensity that some of these would attain.

****

In February we were off again to London. Celebrity support and the ensuing media coverage was still an important factor for us in terms of fundraising and this was undoubtedly one of Sylvia Ingham's strengths. She had organized a glittering Awards Ceremony at the Savoy Hotel at which we recognized and rewarded the support given to us by celebrities, businesses and volunteers. The occasion was sponsored by our President, Lady Pilkington, hosted by Gloria Hunniford and attended by Sir John Mills, Sir Harry Secombe, Sir Cliff Richard, Sally Burton, Faith Brown, Robert Powell, Jean Boht, Joe Brown and many others.

Awards were given to the Littlewoods Organisation, Coca Cola Schweppes, Sir Cliff and Robert Powell, as well as to the Lions Organisation, Scottish and Newcastle Breweries, the Liverpool Daily Post and Echo and the Merseyside Fire Service. Support Group of the year was given to the Isle of Man group who were a model for others in their set up and achievements. Their award was received by Lady Jones who had continued to support the charity after the death of her husband, Sir Lawrence, immediate past Governor of the Island.

Sylvia followed this in March with the Reuters Ball at the Grosvenor Hotel, Park Lane, attended by 1000 people and raising a very large sum of money. At that time we were clearly developing a real presence in London and raising our profile there. It was, however, an expensive scene and we were beginning to stretch ourselves a bit too much. With larger resources behind us we might have gone on to establish ourselves in London but most of our funds were required for and dedicated to the building of the research centre and the research to be carried out there. There was a fine line and we were not, in due course, able to cross it. Time would see our office closed in London, mainly because we were unable to put the investment in to sustain it.

****

Our rapid growth raised concerns for the trustees and Brian Case proposed that our organizational structure should be examined in detail by a small group of trustees and outside individual advisors. This was approved and a small group was established to "review the Foundation as a business operation and make recommendations". Over the next few years this would have far reaching consequences for everyone involved in the charity.

Early in May, I was in America to be elected to the American Association for Thoracic Surgery, a great honour and recognition by my peers of my work as a thoracic surgeon. It had nothing to do with the Foundation although I took every opportunity to tell everyone about the work that was being done in Liverpool.

We had, for some time, been on tenterhooks waiting to hear the result of our bid for £3.5M funding from the National Lottery. On 15 May we received a letter from the Millennium Commission telling us that we had been unsuccessful. This was a major blow, following on from our failure to obtain funds from the European Objective One initiative. Why would no one in public office help us? The reason we were given this time was that our project was not as distinctive as other projects. This was unbelievable and provoked another public outrage. We were building the world's only lung cancer centre. How much more distinctive could you get than that?

We were pioneering a major research programme, supported by distinguished cancer scientists around the world, into the most common form of cancer, with the highest mortality of any cancer, in a region where the incidence of the disease was very high and which constituted a very serious public health problem for the country as a whole. The Centre would also develop a much needed patient care programme and be the home of our smoking cessation activities with both adults and children.

I have no doubt that if we had been researching AIDS or a more popular form of cancer, then we would have been successful but lung cancer was still the Cinderella cancer and lung cancer patients and their families were still being deprived of funds and resources. This latest disappointment exemplified in crystal clear fashion why it had been necessary for me to set the charity up in the first place and reaffirmed my resolve not to give up. After all, I was still seeing the devastating effects of lung cancer every day of my working life. But it was hard to take and we were all very upset.

Sylvia Ingham and one of our Patrons managed to get a meeting with Jennifer Page, the Chief Executive of the Millennium Commission, to talk about our failed application but came away empty handed and disillusioned. They formed the impression of "a dragon", "with no heart", who was not even prepared to discuss the project as such. Their view was that it was unlikely that any future application would be successful and that it would be pointless to waste any further money in this way.

Nevertheless, later in the year we did apply to the Charities Board, another division of the National Lottery, for funding to undertake a national study which would establish once and for all the link between passive smoking and lung cancer. We did this in association with a well known and nationally respected chest physician but were once again refused. We were becoming somewhat paranoid by this time and could not help wondering if "tobacco money" was active behind the scenes although we had no evidence for this. The general public was angry, particularly when they could see how some of the lottery funding was being distributed.

****

The Foundation Stone of the building was laid by Fiona on 29 May 1996 amid a great deal of excitement and carnival atmosphere with a jazz band, a gospel choir, balloons and stilt walkers. Celebrities present included Robert Powell, Wendy Craig, Ken Dodd and Mike McCartney. We were all very much aware of what we owed to Roy and he had said that although he would not be around in person, he would be very much there in spirit. And he was!

Fiona said "Roy said right at the start of the campaign that if he was alive for this day a big sunbeam would shine down on the centre. As I drove into the site the sun started to shine and I thought that was significant. This is a very proud day for me and for Liverpool". She added "I think Roy would have been thrilled – in his own words, gobsmacked!"

Fireman Peter McAdam, whose brother Bob died of lung cancer just before Roy, was also there with Bob's widow Moira and daughter Catherine. Peter said "It's a very poignant day for us because when Roy met Bob he asked him to lay the Foundation Stone with him. Bob was very moved. It should have been Roy and Bob."

Naturally I also felt a real sense of achievement and gratitude to everyone who had made the day possible. But it is relatively easy to lay foundation stones. It is much more difficult to finish a mission successfully.

A second stone was laid by John Moores in recognition of the immense contribution made by the Littlewoods Organisation to the success of the project.

****

During the summer I wrote a nomination for Sylvia to be named National Fundraiser of the Year by the Institute of Charity Fundraising Managers. She was successful and the award was well merited. She had worked hard and effectively to bring the charity to the forefront of public awareness, using innovative techniques and raising millions of pounds in the process.

In June, our International Scientific Advisory Board came again to Liverpool where John Field had arranged in the University a symposium entitled "Current Aspects of Lung Cancer – An International Perspective". It was well attended by scientists and doctors from the UK and abroad. The Advisory Board took the opportunity again to review our research programme and the plans that were being put in place for the Liverpool Lung Project which would be the basis for our whole research effort over the next ten years. They also passed comment on the design and equipment proposals for the laboratories to be built in the Roy Castle Research Centre.

About this time Sylvia was beginning to develop her plans for a World Tour the following year, taking the message of the Foundation far and wide around the globe. It was ambitious and expensive but she convinced the trustees that the financial rewards would be significant. She had the support of Baroness Lynda Chalker who promised to liaise with the British embassies in the countries visited and of Granada Television who would send a film crew as part of a programme on the Foundation which would be broadcast nationally.

The Tour was an outstanding success in many respects but took up an enormous amount of time and energy of our fundraising staff to the detriment of our other fundraising efforts and the development of a sound, long lasting fundraising strategy. As trustees we should have recognized this more clearly than we did at the time but it was difficult to turn back from such an exciting and high profile initiative once it had started rolling. Still, that is what trustees are for and, as Chairman at the time, I have to take most responsibility.

****

We continued to expand the organization by appointing a telesales manager, who was not to last long, a national sports events manager, mainly for golf but also for some other high profile sports events and we advertised for a legacy manager and a regional fundraiser for Merseyside.

More importantly we drew up the job specification for a finance manager, although Sylvia had resisted this for some time on the basis that we did not have room in the office for such a person. The appointment was made in October and the post taken up in November but, before long, the appointee had fallen out with Sylvia and the trustees were forced to end his appointment. Brian Case vowed that this should never happen again and a replacement finance manager, George Aldridge, was appointed to implement the financial controls and procedures agreed by the trustees. George held the position for several years, including the most difficult and traumatic time in the history of the charity. It wasn't an easy job but he made a good fist of it and was very loyal to me when I needed it most.

Dr Judith Youngson took up her appointment on 1 October as Director of Epidemiology, having been interviewed by Professors Field, Bishop and Crampton, all very senior and experienced university research people. She was to do an excellent job in overcoming all the practical difficulties of setting up the Liverpool Lung Project, an extremely complex project involving patients, GPs, surgeons, physicians, high risk individuals, pathologists, health authorities, ethical committees and much more. She had innumerable problems to resolve and did so with great perseverance and application to detail. She also had responsibility for producing academic papers from the epidemiological department and this was to prove more difficult for her.

****

On 11 August 1996, the trustees discussed and then agreed a proposal from me to visit Glasgow with a view to developing the Foundation there. I saw a great opportunity for us in Glasgow, not just because it was my home city, but because it resembled Liverpool in so many ways. It had a huge lung cancer problem and my view was that the people there were such that they would understand our objectives and respond in a generous fashion, just as the people of Liverpool had done. A major difference, which should work in our favour, was that, although they shared the same problems, there was much more wealth in Glasgow to address them.

Sylvia was not so keen and I can still see her furrowed brow when she was asked for her opinion. However, the trustees went along with my wishes and I began to plan our first visit.

July 1994. Saying goodbye to Roy at the start of the Tour of Hope. He was so ill I was not certain that I would see him again.

The launch of the street poster campaign in 1993. Roy has his arm around Lynne Bell who came up with the strap line 'Cause for Hope'.

Roy with Roger and Jean Healey, who led the Aughton and Ormskirk support group for over ten years.

With my daughter Catherine, who held the charity together in its first few years.

Lady Mavis Pilkington with (left to right) Rod Walker (trustee) Les Howell (trustee) Professor Peter Toyne, patron, and Bill Matthews (trustee). The occasion was a fundraising concert by the Royal Liverpool Philharmonic Orchestra compered by BBC newsreader Richard Baker.

Traveling by train on the Tour of Hope. Very ill but invariably positive and cheerful.

Appearing for the last time on stage at the Empire Theatre the night before the Tour of Hope started in Liverpool. Roy was so weak that Sir John Mills did not think he could possibly walk on to the stage. But he did!

At Waterloo Station at the end of the Tour of Hope. It's hard to believe that within six weeks Roy would no longer be with us.

Signing the agreement with the City Council to acquire the land for the Research Centre. Architect Stephen Quicke is second right at the back.

Terry Kavanagh (centre) with Johnny Kennedy (immediate right) prior to a fundraising run through Liverpool City Centre. On the left, from the outside, are Paula Chadwick, Debbie Rollinson and Trish Dodd. On the right are George Aldridge, Cath Steele and Liz Legge.

With Elizabeth at a fundraising event in Glasgow.

Glad rags! This was taken after receiving my Honorary Fellowship from Liverpool John Moores University. Left to right, Professor Peter Toyne, Vice Chancellor, my wife Elizabeth and Sir Philip Carter, Pro-Chancellor and chairman of Governors. Sir Philip would later become chairman of the Foundation.

Home at last. The return to Liverpool Lime Street station after the World Tour which had taken the message of the Foundation to five continents and 12 major cities.

Fiona with Nelson Mandela during the World Tour. He was thrilled to hold the famous FA Cup and we were more than thrilled to tell him about the work of the Foundation.

Tessa Jowell, Public Health Minister, after receiving a special Roy Castle Foundation Award for her efforts in introducing a complete ban on tobacco advertising in the UK. Pictured at the Awards ceremony with Gloria Hunniford and Sir Cliff Richard.

Hats off to the new Professor! Vice Chancellor Peter Toyne on the right.

Football superstars Alan Hansen and Gary Linacre handing over a cheque for £750,000 from Littlewoods.

Work begins on clearing the site for the world's first lung cancer research centre.

The research centre takes shape.

After the ceremony of laying the Foundation Stone, the celebrities attending got together for this group photograph. Ken Dodd seems preoccupied!

The finished article!
A beautiful work of
architecture and one
which would have
thrilled Roy Castle.

With Sir Cliff and
Fiona at the opening of
the Research Centre.

Frankie Vaughan opens
the Cold Storage room in
the research centre. The
room was fitted out with
money donated by the
Grand Order of Water
Rats of which Frankie
was King Rat. The
caption on the wall was
inaccurate in that Roy
had never actually been
King Rat.

With Sylvia Ingham, Sir Cliff and Fiona after Sir Cliff had carried out the official opening of the Roy Castle International Centre for Lung Cancer Research.

Robert Powell, whose father died of lung cancer and a long term supporter of the charity, is pictured with Dr Judith Youngson after opening the Epidemiology Unit in the Research Centre.

Ken Dodd, giving out a powerful anti-smoking message in his own inimitable way.

Wall hanging number 1. This colourful work of art, created by Janet Haigh, combining embroidery, appliqué, photocopying and patchwork, commemorates the early history of the charity in terms some of the people who made it happen. Pictured in the centre are Sheila Christian and Eric Morris who sat with me in my office for the first ever meeting of the Lung Cancer Fund on 18 April 1990.

Wall hanging number 2. Also created by Janet Haigh, this commemorates the Roy Castle years and the change from the Lung Cancer Fund to the Roy Castle Lung Cancer Foundation. Both hangings can be seen in the Research Centre with explanatory text alongside.

Fiona opening our charity shop in Formby. On her right is Pat Tisdale, our Director of Retail, and on the left Pat Gibbons, shop manager. The Formby shop has been one of our most successful.

With Cherie Blair and Sir David Hunt at the 10 Downing Street reception hosted by Mrs Blair.

Successful fundraising group 'Ladies Link' with (left to right) Joy Hilton, Cath Maxwell, my wife Elizabeth and Sheila Lupton.

The Fag Ends team. Their success in helping people to stop smoking is as good as anyones and better than most.

The Fundraising team. Without the hard work and dedication of our fundraisers, nothing else would be possible. Everyone in research, patient care and tobacco control depends upon their success and the generosity of our supporters.

Our Senior Management Team. *Back row left to right:* Joyce Dunlop (Patient Care), Mike Grundy (Finance), Asaf Niaz (IT), Dr Jesme Baird (Medical Director), Mike Unger (Chief Executive).
Front row left to right: Paul Gauntlett (Development), Christine Owens (Tobacco Control), Pat Tisdale (Retail), Paula Chadwick (Personnel), Prof John Field (Research).

I wrote to Professor Sir Graeme Davies, Principal and Vice Chancellor of the University, who had previously been Vice Chancellor of the University of Liverpool and a Patron of the Lung Cancer Fund. When he had left Liverpool some years before to take up a post in London, he had written to me to ask whether he should resign as a Patron of the charity. I had said that he should continue because we did not know what the future might bring!

Sir Graeme responded very warmly to my letter indicating our wish to develop the Foundation in Glasgow and, in so doing, to have close links with the University. He discussed my request with Professor Stan Kaye, head of oncology and cancer research. He, in turn, requested Dr David Dunlop, NHS clinical oncologist in Glasgow, to liaise with us. David was to become a trustee, a firm friend in difficult times, chairman of our Grants Committee and a huge influence on the development of the Foundation in Glasgow and elsewhere.

I rang David for the first time on 4 September 1996 and reassured him of our commitment to the development of a significant programme in Glasgow and that a sizable amount of the money raised there would be spent there. I indicated that, as I saw it, our main focus in Glasgow should be on the clinical side of lung cancer in terms of treatment of the disease and management of its consequences for patients and their families. This would complement our work in Liverpool which was pure research into the development of lung cancer. We discussed an agenda for a visit in November to meet Sir Graeme Davies as well as the Dean of the Medical School, the Professor of Oncology, various chest physicians interested in lung cancer, oncology nurses and perhaps some patients. It would be important to get the politics right and not to step on sensitive toes!

* * * * * * * * * * * * * *

Meanwhile work was proceeding on the construction of the research centre in Liverpool although a six week delay had developed due to difficulties with the drum roof which had unique architectural features. I was involved in many of the numerous meetings which took place between the Foundation, the architect, the builders and other contractors as well as with the University regarding facilities management and other issues, the city council, various providers of utility services and scientists involved in or advising on the project.

At their meeting in October 1996, the trustees reviewed our financial position. After taking into account all our commitments, our asset balance stood at £1.4M and income continued at £36,000 a week plus the very large sums which we were receiving on a regular basis from Littlewoods Lotteries. Deloitte Touche were preparing our statutory accounts and we had asked them to look at our financial controls. This latter was something about which the trustees remained concerned and kept coming back to since, although we felt that proper controls had been established, we were not sure that they were being fully complied with or enforced. It would be three more years before the lid blew off.

Sylvia Ingham reported to the trustees that she had met with the former Head of Retailing at the Imperial Cancer Research Fund and that she was looking at the possibility of a nationwide chain of Roy Castle charity shops. In the first place, a pilot scheme was being put together for 20 shops in Cumbria and south-west Scotland to be managed by her friend Carol Milnes. This was a very ambitious proposal and the trustees were wary but to some extent reassured by the quality of advice which she seemed to have taken. It was decided that no decision would be taken until a formal presentation had been made.

Sylvia also reported on progress of her plans for a World Tour, taking the message of the Foundation to North America, Japan, Australia, Hong Kong, Dubai, South Africa and Europe. This was a hugely imaginative proposal which would raise the profile of lung cancer in many countries where this was greatly needed and, of course, the Foundation would also benefit in terms of the huge amount of publicity which this would generate. Littlewoods had received approval for us to take the FA Cup with us throughout the Tour (which proved very popular at every stop) and Baroness Lynda Chalker had begun writing to all the British embassies and consulates in the various cities where the Tour would stop.

Some sponsorship from Littlewoods had been promised and some of the flights would be donated by Virgin Airways. Apart from this there were no firm guarantee that the Tour would raise sufficient funds to cover its costs and compensate for the time spent on the project by our fundraising team in the months leading up to the Tour, and during the Tour itself, which could have been used for income generation in more conventional ways.

It was reasonable to expect that the proposed Tour would be at least as successful as the previous two UK tours but uncertain budgets were produced and no detailed profit and loss sheet prepared. As trustees we should have insisted on these but we were carried along by the opportunities that the Tour would give to raise the profile of lung cancer far beyond Liverpool and the UK, the invaluable publicity benefits to the Foundation, the fact that so many of the arrangements had already been put in place by Sylvia and her previous record of successful fundraising through Tours with Roy and Fiona.

As will be told later, the World Tour achieved many of its important objectives in spectacular fashion but it did not make money and, in fact, was a significant cost to the Foundation. Sylvia did point out to us that Littlewoods Pools had pledged a further five scratch card games at a value of £1.2M but it is likely that we would have received this anyway, such was the commitment of Littlewoods to the Foundation at that time and afterwards.

****

Shortly after this, we used a recruitment agency to help us appoint a fundraiser for London. From a strong group of candidates we selected Pauline Hunt who was working for the Parkinsons Society and appeared to be a safe pair of hands with a good track record and significant legacy experience.

On 23 October, I met with the organisational review committee which the trustees had set up to examine the Foundation as a business and make appropriate recommendations. We shared a desire to review my role and I was anxious to ensure that they understood well the nature of the Foundation and its mission and to express my own concerns in some areas.

At that time I was still Chairman and Medical Director of the Foundation, Director designate of the Research Centre, link person with both the University of Liverpool and Liverpool John Moores University, main spokesman in the media, chairman of the charity's Grants Committee and link with all our Patrons as well as being heavily involved in fundraising through support groups and functions and in giving support and advice to Sylvia Ingham. At the same time, I had a busy surgical practice to run. Something had to change, not least because, in my view, I was probably not the best person to fill any of those roles. My expertise was as a surgeon and I had always seen myself as filling several roles within the charity until the right, properly qualified, person came along.

The Foundation had grown at an explosive rate which accounted to some extent for the difficulties we were having in controlling all aspects of the charity and it had reached a stage where it needed a professional chairman with experience of business practice and procedure. In fact, it could be said that it had needed this for some time. This was agreed by the committee and also that, for the time being, it would be in the best interests of the charity for me to continue as Medical Director.

I expressed to them my concern at the lack of financial expertise within the Foundation. We were well served at trustee level but there was no-one with sufficient knowledge and authority in the office to ensure proper financial planning and control. This had also been a concern of the trustees for some time. In addition we needed some legal expertise and more medical input and I asked for clarification on the responsibilities of trustees with regard to delegation of authority.

The view was expressed that the role of chief executive of a charity was not like that of a normal business and that the trustees needed a measure of control. The roles of chief executive and Head of Fundraising should be separated and the trustees should be the policy making board. We discussed the composition of a future management group to run the charity on a day to day basis.

Sylvia Ingham was discussed and she was considered to be highly competent and motivated and "learning as she goes". She was thought at times to be too ambitious and optimistic, with too many irons in the fire and sometimes having to rein back at a cost to the Foundation. I recognized some of these faults in myself. She did not like writing reports and budgets were not her strong point. It was felt that the Foundation was vulnerable without a clear deputy to Sylvia and there was no one on the staff at that time who was suitable for the role. This had still not been rectified three years later when the deficiency was startlingly exposed.

****

The next day I was in Brussels visiting the Institut Bordet for a meeting with Dr Sculier, a chest physician who was leading a European Working Party on the early diagnosis of lung cancer. His interest was mainly clinical and not in the area of basic science that we were pursuing in Liverpool. The contact however was a valuable one and provided an opportunity to talk about the work of the Foundation to Dr Sculier and his colleagues.

Whilst in Brussels I visited the British Ambassador in Brussels, David Colvin, and his wife Caroline. They had just arrived from Rome where they had spent the last five years and were still unpacking boxes when I walked in. They made me very welcome and, over a nice cup of tea, we discussed arrangements for a reception at the EU embassy during the World Tour the following year.

****

It was on 7 November 1996 that we made our first and, in some ways, historic visit to Glasgow. Sylvia and I flew up from Manchester and were an hour late because of delays in the plane coming down from Edinburgh to Manchester. We were met by David Dunlop. A couple of early meetings had to be cancelled because of our late arrival and we had to go straight into our presentations in the main lecture theatre at the Western Infirmary (where, incidentally, I believe that my father died of cancer when I was eight years old).

The atmosphere was rather dingy but there were about 20 people there, including representatives from Macmillan Cancer Relief, the Cancer Research Campaign and Bacup as well as chest physicians, oncologists, senior nurses and patients. I spoke first but no-one introduced me before I got up and I was unsure of the audience, being conscious of the possibility that we could be seen as intruders on the local charity scene.

There was a chest physician present who looked thoroughly miserable and unwelcoming, who scarcely looked up from his notes and asked a lot of awkward questions. I dealt with him politely and forcefully and was amazed after the meeting when he came up to me smiling and offered to help in any way he could!

In my speech I outlined the roots, activities and ambitions of the Foundation and showed a video which confirmed these. I then described the opportunities for the Foundation in Glasgow to promote an extensive and vigorous campaign of clinical research, education and patient support. This was well received.

Sylvia then spoke about the reasons for her own involvement, about

Roy Castle and about the organization and touched on the World Tour. She spoke very fluently and well and the audience were clearly moved by this and by a video which she showed on some of the special events she had organized in her time with the Foundation.

David Dunlop then invited questions, many of which centered around the sensitivities of other cancer charities and the strong desire of those present that money raised in Glasgow should result in lung cancer investment in Glasgow. I reassured them at length of our very strong commitment to develop our work in Glasgow, not pound for pound but for approved and agreed projects. I said that it could even be that we would spend more in Glasgow than we raised, not realizing how true this would become over the next few years.

Over a buffet lunch we had the opportunity to mix with the people attending. Isobel, a lung cancer patient, and her husband Hamish, a professional painter, were enthusiastic to help. Professor Stan Kaye, head of medical oncology in Glasgow and funded by the Cancer Research Campaign, was fortunately very supportive since it would have been very difficult for us to make any headway in Glasgow without him. Phyllis Campbell, nurse manager of oncology at the Western Hospital and a much respected and experienced person, was enthusiastic and offered to join a fundraising committee. Morag McIntosh, head of fundraising in Glasgow for Macmillan Cancer Relief, was particularly impressed by the presentations and would later come to work for the Foundation as head of our Glasgow office.

Also present and fired up with enthusiasm was someone who would go on to do great things for the Foundation and make a massive contribution to its development not only in Glasgow or the UK but worldwide. Dr Jesme Baird was working as a Staff Grade Registrar in the Oncology Centre at the Western Infirmary. Intelligent, dynamic, attractive and with a clear understanding of her subject, she was captivated by what we were proposing to do and very willing to help. She had been particularly impressed by Sylvia but, sadly, this admiration would not stand the test of time. I recognized talents that could be of enormous benefit to the Foundation and, in due course, would recruit her as my full time assistant medical director. Later she would become our Director of Patient Care and establish this aspect of our work on the international stage. It was a good day for lung cancer patients and their families when Jesme and I met in Glasgow.

After lunch, Sylvia went off to the airport to return to Liverpool whilst David and I went to the University to meet Sir Graeme Davies, Principal of the University of Glasgow, and we spent a magnificent half hour with him. He indicated his willingness to help in any way he could. He would start by hosting the launch of the Foundation in Glasgow at a reception in the Hunterian Museum followed by lunch in the Banqueting Hall. He would try to provide us with office accommodation in the university and asked that Sylvia should get in touch with him about this. He said that he would firmly support the various proposals we were putting forward in Glasgow.

Later in the afternoon, I went with David to the Royal Victoria Hospital for a meeting with Dr Mike Soukop, head of oncology and Dr Steve Banham, chest physician. They seemed to be a harmonious team and I was encouraged by their uncomplicated attitudes. We discussed the possibility of the Foundation funding a Senior Lecturer in the department of oncology under Professor Stan Kaye and we spent a long time talking about a possible "flagship project" for the Foundation in Glasgow.

Our ideas began to crystallize around a lung cancer clinical research unit in the university department, based at the Royal, with a research nurse and back-up to conduct clinical trials into the latest advances in treatment of lung cancer. The cost of drugs and the "hotel" costs of the beds would be paid for by the hospital but we would purchase equipment and provide statistical and secretarial support. The unit would also serve as a base for epidemiological studies as well as stop smoking campaigns with children and low income groups. Collaboration with our laboratories in Liverpool would be through the provision of lung cancer samples from patients to help determine resistance and sensitivities to drugs used in treatment.

As I write this nearly nine years later, none of this has come to pass for a number of reasons, mainly lack of funds but I am still hopeful because of people like Jamie Rae, whose business has raised large sums of money for the Foundation, whose parents both died of lung cancer and who now, as a volunteer, leads our Development Group in Glasgow. Other activities in Glasgow, however, have already developed to a remarkable degree and made an impact far beyond the town of my birth.

David Dunlop took me to the airport the following morning and appeared very enthusiastic. He is a highly respected oncologist with a very clear mind and a good academic brain. He also obviously cared a lot for his patients and would prove to be a most valuable ally and friend of the Foundation as it went through an important period of growth and development. He would also become a trustee and chairman of our grants committee and provide that extra medical input which the Organisational Review Committee had requested.

****

During November, a series of detailed meetings took place with the University of Liverpool about the new building. Management facilities, security, equipment purchase, cabling for IT, telephones, gardening, window cleaning, sewerage, building fabric and engineering service, insurance, utilities, etc, etc. All these had to be sorted out and I found some of them quite baffling. Terry Malone proved invaluable in reaching agreement with the University on all these issues and, because of the huge amount of time he was spending on the project in all its aspects, he agreed to stand down as a trustee to take up the role, for three and a half days a week, of project manager for the scheme. He did a superb job, keeping costs down and negotiating with the builders and professionals involved as well as with the local authorities and other providers of services.

Money was saved by removing the proposed glazed panelling from the balustrade on the stairs and by not panelling the Exhibition Room. A donation of £10,000 had been received from the Sir Alastair Pilkington Trust to equip one of the smaller laboratories. United Utilities donated £3000 and Manweb reduced the cost of providing the sub-station from £11,000 to £500.

We were informed that the building contract was four weeks behind schedule but would be completed by the end of April 1997. The equipping period would follow and the Foundation and epidemiology staff would be able to move in during July with the laboratories available for use in September. An area of land adjacent to the site was available for purchase and we had made a bid for it. This would prove successful and we were subsequently able to extend our car parking space.

****

On 16 November, I flew out to Africa for a lecture tour arranged by the Royal College of Surgeons of Edinburgh and the Association of

Surgeons of East and Central Africa. I was to visit six countries in three weeks including Uganda, Kenya, Mozambique, Tanzania, South Africa and Zimbabwe, lecturing and teaching postgraduate and undergraduate students. In Kampala, I saw a couple of my own patients who had traveled to Liverpool for surgery and was pleased to find them well.

Wherever I went, I spoke about the Roy Castle Foundation and the work it was doing. Lung cancer is not yet a major problem in these countries but it will be one day when life expectancy increases and the effects of uncontrolled tobacco promotion and advertising take their toll. One of my ambitions is that, by the time the lung cancer epidemic comes to Africa and other developing nations, as it undoubtedly will, we will have found the answers and be able to prevent and cure it. The work of the Foundation has world wide implications.

My tour finished with a lecture at the annual meeting of the Association of Surgeons of East and Central Africa, the guest of honour being Robert Mugabe! His reputation was then still reasonably intact and I am ashamed to say that I have a photograph of me shaking hands with him as he presented me with an illuminated scroll and a gold medallion provide by the Royal College of Surgeons of Edinburgh. At least he thought that he was giving me a Gold Medal since it had been stolen in the baggage handling at Nairobi Airport. The box had not been taken and we had decided to go ahead with the presentation since he had been told that he would do this and the organizers were afraid to tell him what had happened. They told me to be absolutely certain that I did not open the box!

It had been an amazing journey in which I had learned so much although I was supposed to be the one doing the teaching.

****

Shortly after getting back from Africa, I made my last professional visit to the Isle of Man, where I had been Visiting Thoracic Surgeon since 1977. It was quite a moving occasion for me, and the colleagues and nurses I had worked with over the years held a small reception at which they said some very nice things. I had treated thousands of patients during my time there and had made many friends. It was sad for me but my reason for stepping down was the rapidly increasing workload resulting from the continued expansion of the Foundation. It was a financial sacrifice but I felt that it was well worth it. Mildred Cooper hosted a dinner for about 90 people at her home and a number of patients and their relatives were there. I had become very fond of the Isle of Man and fortunately have been able to maintain the friendships forged over nearly 20 years.

✳✳✳✳✳✳✳✳✳✳✳✳✳✳

It had been a very busy year and we had made significant progress.

Chapter 22

Nearly There

A number of good things happened early in 1997. From my own point of view I was delighted and much relieved that the trustees agreed to the appointment of a Personal Assistant for me. There is no doubt that this was long overdue and, on 21 February, we appointed Paula Chadwick. As well as doing an outstanding job for me and an absolute rock in times of trouble, she would prove to be of immense value to the whole of the Foundation taking on more and more senior responsibilities within the charity as time went by, in an untiring, cheerful and efficient manner. On the same day I interviewed Debbie Rollinson and spotted some real talent. I recommended her to Sylvia Ingham and she was appointed as her assistant. She did a great job for the Foundation but I am afraid unwittingly I had given her something of a poisoned chalice.

About this time, Dr Teresa Knapp was firmly identified as the laboratory manager, an appointment which ensured the efficient acquisition and installation of all the very expensive and sophisticated equipment in the new laboratories. Teresa had previously set up and managed a molecular laboratory in the Liverpool School of Tropical Medicine and her experience proved invaluable. Her knowledge of the industry and her ability to negotiate resulted in savings of several hundred thousand pounds in equipment purchase.

We also received news that Sir Cliff Richard had agreed to open the Centre when appropriate and Terry Malone confirmed that the handover of the building would take place in early May. So many important events in the history of the Foundation have taken place in May and, indeed, Cliff was to open the centre in May of the following year. When I wrote to Cliff inviting him to do this and asking him whether he would agree to us putting his name on the main laboratory in the Centre, I received a handwritten reply expressing his sense of privilege and the thrill that he felt to have his name attached to a scientific laboratory. It was certainly a first for him and, as far as I am aware, the only time he has been honoured in this way.

* * * * * * * * * * * * * *

In February, I went over to Brussels with John Field and Sylvia Ingham for a meeting with European Commissioner Padraig Flynn, whose brief included all matters related to public health. He received us very warmly. He was the prime mover in the European Commission in trying to establish a European Directive to ban tobacco advertising throughout the member countries. He was very nearly successful, being thwarted at the last minute by the Germans and the Spanish. We explained to him our view that lung cancer was a children's disease since they were the new smokers of today, it being very rare nowadays for an adult to start smoking. We made a firm friend that day and he would go on to recommend us to the British Government for support and would speak in London at a conference I organized the following year.

While in Brussels we met with Dr Bill Baig, a principal scientific officer in the EU, whose role was to appraise cancer research applications for European funding. It was a splendid meeting which would bear much fruit in years to come. He told us that on his desk he had 300 grant applications for cancer research, 150 of which were state of the art, but, he said, that what we were doing was of great interest to him and had enormous potential not only for lung cancer but also for other groups researching other cancers. This was very reassuring and encouraging since we were ploughing a lonely furrow with our research programme in the UK. He gave us some useful practical advice and assurance of his interest and support. John Field in particular has maintained a close relationship with him over the years.

In May, we received our second European grant to work with children. £120,000 was committed to us by the EU's public health directorate for a programme, which we had put together and would manage, entitled "A European Approach to Smoking Prevention in Pre-adolescent Children". It would involve primary schools in the UK, France and Portugal and was aimed at helping children to develop skills which would enable them to resist smoking in later years. Sue Occulston was the originator of the programme and we had already supported her in a similar scheme in primary schools in the Knowsley district of Merseyside. It was based on the Child to Child approach, now called Shared Learning in Action, whereby children were encouraged to learn from each other rather than being fed information by adults. In spite of the language difficulties, the project was successfully completed two years later and the results published in a report.

At the trustees' meeting on 24 February, I proposed a small but, in my view, important change to the name of the charity. It seemed sensible to include the words 'lung cancer' in our title so that it might be clear to all potential supporters what our purpose was and which disease we were targeting. This might have seemed unnecessary just then but, as time went by and the Roy Castle name faded, particularly among a generation who had not known him as an entertainer, we would come to rely more and more on those directly affected by lung cancer and their families and friends, as in fact we had done in the early days before Roy came on board. Sylvia was not so keen on the change, preferring to retain the title 'The Roy Castle Cause for Hope Foundation', which had a good marketing ring about it, but the trustees agreed with me and we decided to approach the Charity Commission with a view to changing our name to The Roy Castle Lung Cancer Foundation.

Brian Case then presented the final report of the Organisational Review Committee along the lines already described. This was approved with a view to implementation as soon as possible. A new committee would be formed, the Finance and General Purposes Committee, chaired by myself as Chairman, and composed of the Chief Executive, the Finance Executive and one other trustee. The purpose of this committee would be to bridge the gap between trustees and management, allowing the trustees to begin to delegate more responsibility to the management team and speed up decision making on behalf of the Board of Trustees.

It was also agreed, at last, that we would make firm moves to recruit a new chairman and allow me to concentrate solely on my role as Medical Director. I had wanted this for a long time but it would be another 18 months before we found the right man. I had some leadership qualities but I knew that I did not have the experience or skills to run an expanding business.

At the same meeting, John Field presented for approval a full outline, with costs for the next three years, of the Liverpool Lung Project, the research programme to be carried out in the Centre. The trustees now had a clear definition of its aims which were to identify individuals at high risk of developing lung cancer and to determine the fingerprint of lung cancer, that is the sequence of changes in the genes of the lung cells caused by tobacco and other agents and which leads to lung cancer. The programme had the full backing of our International Advisory Board and the trustees agreed to continue to fund it. On his part, John agreed to provide two annual reports, one scientific and one in language that the trustees could understand!

Ed Stanley was proposed and agreed as a new trustee. Ed was an IT specialist with strong commercial experience and would play a pivotal role in the events of two years later.

We also agreed to purchase, for £40,000, an area of land adjacent to the Centre which would significantly increase our car parking but more importantly allow for possible future extensions.

Sylvia spoke again about the World Tour and predicted a surplus of £183,000 without counting any contribution from Littlewoods Lotteries. In the event this failed to materialise although the Tour was highly successful in other ways.

****

Two days later I was in Glasgow again. We had lunch with the Principal of the University, Sir Graeme Davies, and once again he was extremely supportive. We discussed the political difficulties involved in setting up a Roy Castle Clinical Research Unit and Sir Graeme advised us to speak to the Dean of Medicine. We asked how we could get a meeting with him and he then went to his window, saw that the Dean's car was still there, went out of the room and brought him back! We had a lengthy and valuable discussion in which we were able to describe to him the project and the benefits to the University. At the end he said that he would take it to the University Cancer Research Committee with "a powerful steer" and determination to see it go through. Most of the funding for this would have to be raised in Scotland and, sadly, we are still waiting for this to happen.

A lively, warm and historic meeting took place that afternoon with a group of David Dunlop's patients, Jim and Barbara Elliot, Tom and Helen Haswell, Isabel and Hamish Montgomery. The purpose of the meeting was for me to tell them about my ideas for forming a network of patient support groups and how we could supply much needed information and relevant literature. The first thing to do was to form a group in Glasgow and their reaction was positive and heartwarming. Jim and Tom, both of whom spoke very powerfully, had each been diagnosed some time before with inoperable lung cancer but had managed to survive thanks to the skills and dedication of David Dunlop. Jesme Baird was also present and they all agreed to give it further thought.

Support groups were quite common for many cancers although there were none for lung cancer. My plan was not only to establish patient supports groups in all the main cancer centres across the UK but to bring them together in a network which would provide a voice for those affected by this most neglected of cancers. I was used to government ministers and others receiving me politely but in the end doing nothing substantial. If we could only get a proportion of the 40,000 people affected by lung cancer every year to form one voice and to lobby politicians, health authorities and the media, there was every chance that they would receive a hearing and be able to effect changes in the provision of health care and the funding of basic scientific research.

Barbara was the first to commit herself, over a cup of coffee in her kitchen with Jesme Baird. From that moment the patient care initiative of the Foundation has grown and expanded until it now has an international dimension. Barbara's husband, Jim, sadly died of the disease but not before he had made his mark with the developing initiative. Barbara has been remarkable in her ability to communicate effectively with all kinds of groups and organizations and I have no doubt that Jim would be very proud of her. Tom Haswell has so far survived 13 years and has become a powerful advocate for lung cancer patients, serving on several important health committees in Scotland to ensure that their voice is heard and speaking powerfully at lung cancer conferences.

Initially under my direction and then subsequently and substantially under that of Jesme Baird, the Patient Care Division of the Foundation has become an effective and widely respected voice for lung cancer patients, providing extensive information and literature for those diagnosed with the disease and looking after more than 25 lung cancer patient support groups in cancer centres around the country. It is shocking to think that none of this was available before the Roy Castle Foundation came along. Because lung cancer tends to affect those who are already disadvantaged in society and because on the whole their survival is so poor, patients with the disease have historically been at the end of the queue when it comes to provision of services and access to the latest forms of investigation and treatment. It has not helped that the disease is seen to be self inflicted although our hospitals are filled with other diseases which are clearly self inflicted but which do not carry the same stigma. The situation is slowly changing now and much of the credit for this must be given to those within the Foundation who are working so hard to make things better.

****

Towards the end of February, Norman Cowley, a businessman in Liverpool, agreed to donate £10,000 for a work of art in the new Centre and, in due course, this crystallized into the idea of a statue of Roy to be commissioned from famous Liverpool sculptor Stephen Broadbent.

The London Road Development Agency had also offered £10,000 for a work of art in the Centre and I held a series of meetings with their representative, Sara Warner, and with Frances Downey of the Liverpool Design Initiative to decide on the best way forward. Further financial help would come from the North West Arts Board and the Foundation itself. My wife, Elizabeth, proposed that the money should be spent on wall hangings or tapestries and, of the various options, this was the one chosen. My own idea was that they should represent the history of the charity in "people terms", i.e. they should constitute a montage representing individuals who had made a significant contribution to the establishment and development of the organization so that they would never be forgotten.

The commissioning process was managed by the Liverpool Design Initiative and advertisements placed in the national press. Six artists were interviewed and Janet Haig chosen because she impressed as the one most likely to provide the quality required in a bright and cheerful fashion. I provided her with information and photographs of the people to be included and the result was everything we could have wanted. Two hangings were completed using a combination of techniques of hand embroidery, appliqué and patchwork. They can now be viewed in the Exhibition Room at the Roy Castle Centre with appropriate explanatory script alongside and as a permanent reminder of those to whom we owe so much. A lot has happened since then, however, and perhaps it is time for another one!

****

On 29 April, I was in Glasgow again for further discussions on the appointment of a senior research fellow in the University, a lung cancer support nurse at the Beatson Oncology Centre and further development of the patient support group and network. Jesme Baird was now getting her teeth into the last of these and we agreed to meet at the upcoming World Lung Cancer conference in Dublin with patients, relatives and doctors, as well as Peggy McCarthy, inspiration and main mover of ALCASE, an American association promoting the interests of lung cancer patients. We would also get Fiona Castle to attend and see how we could take the initiative forward.

In May, I went to the States for a surgical conference and took advantage of the trip to visit Tobacco Free Kids in Washington. This is one of the most effective and cutting edge anti-tobacco campaigning organizations in the world. I was made very welcome as I described the work we were doing in Liverpool and the plans we had formulated for a Phase 2 extension to the Roy Castle Centre which would be given over entirely to original and imaginative work with children. It had long been my view that all tobacco issues could be more powerfully and effectively argued if they were put in the context of children and their vulnerability to manipulation and harm.

I also attended a lung cancer patient conference at the National Cancer Institute, with live video links to other cities around the States. Doctors and scientists attended this as well as patients and carers and it was a very powerful experience. It gave me the idea to do something similar in the UK.

While in Washington I had meetings with the executive officers of the American Association for Thoracic Surgery, of which I was a member, and we reached agreement to fund an annual scholarship which would allow trainee chest surgeons from the States to come to Liverpool to carry out research in the laboratories of the Roy Castle Centre and to gain surgical experience from spending some time in the operating theatres in Liverpool. There would be several benefits from this, not least that, over a period of time, we would establish a real presence in the United States as the surgeons went on to establish themselves in their profession.

Back home, I was soon into a succession of planning meetings for the fitting out and running of the Centre, the upcoming World Lung Cancer Conference in Dublin, the Scientific Workshop at the Centre which John Field and I were putting together for July and, of course, the World Tour which was almost upon us.

Chapter 23

World Tour

Nine major cities and five continents in just twenty-six days was surely the most ambitious project ever organised by a charity. Sylvia Ingham's astonishing ability to conceive and put together such a spectacular event was quite exceptional and the high profile support she secured for the tour was remarkable.

The World Tour had some very serious aims. The United Kingdom was not the only country where lung cancer patients were grossly undervalued. In fact, this applied to every country in the world including the United States. Our intention was to raise awareness of the seriousness of the problem of lung cancer across the world, of the dearth of funding for research and of the lack of resources available for patients with lung cancer compared to other cancers. We also intended to highlight the many issues associated with smoking tobacco. The mission I had given the Foundation several years before was that we should make a significant contribution to the worldwide effort to prevent and defeat lung cancer and here we were, making real progress towards this and building on partnerships we had already made in other countries.

We set out to forge links with cancer scientists and organisations as well as with specialists and other staff in hospitals treating lung cancer patients and, of course, the patients themselves. We wanted to raise their spirits, bring them a message of hope and tell them about the work of the Foundation in Liverpool but we knew also that we would learn a lot from the people we would meet.

In addition, there would be significant value for the Foundation in retaining important celebrity and corporate support and we could raise money for the Foundation although, in the event, this was mainly indirectly through the publicity and corporate friendships made.

A party of ten, including Robert Powell, Philip Schofield, representatives from the Littlewoods Organisation and Arthur Johnson, an experienced journalist from the *Liverpool Echo* who would send back regular reports, left Heathrow on Monday 19 May 1997, bolstered by a message from Diana, Princess of Wales, to say that her thoughts and prayers were with everyone involved with the Roy Castle

Foundation and wishing us a positive and successful tour. She said that it was vital that all the countries in the world should join together to find a solution to the appalling problem of lung cancer.

Led from the front throughout by Fiona, with great energy and style, the tour was an exhausting but happy and successful event. We were waived off at Heathrow Airport by Richard Branson who had donated the seats on Virgin Atlantic. The FA Cup, the oldest and most famous domestic football trophy in the world, had its own seat and ticket and was to prove a masterstroke during the tour, attracting publicity and bringing smiles of delight to the faces of many people, including some important statesmen, not least Nelson Mandela. The Cup had been put in the charge of Ian Callaghan, one of the most famous past players of Liverpool Football Club. Ian, together with big Andy Hall from Littlewoods, had the heavy responsibility of ensuring that the Cup came to no harm and was returned unscathed.

Accompanying us on the tour was a camera crew from Granada Television. Sylvia had persuaded them to produce a documentary for the Network First series which would have national coverage. Mixed in with scenes of receptions at British Embassies, visits to hospitals, meetings with statesmen, emotional encounters between Fiona and lung cancer patients in South Africa, Hong Kong and the United States, and quiet reflections in far flung places of Roy by Fiona, would be film of me in my clinic in Liverpool talking to patients and telling them they had lung cancer and subsequently taking one of them, Catherine Gonigle, through surgery and recovery.

It proved to be a very powerful programme, highlighting the consequences all around the world of smoking tobacco and the dramatic efforts of the Foundation to address these as it went from continent to continent. And, running like threads throughout the programme, were demonstrated, in stark terms, the very reasons for the existence of the Foundation as I dealt with my patients, telling them the diagnosis they did not want to hear and then removing a lung cancer from Catherine's chest

Because I still had my job to do, and in order to film the clinical part of the programme concurrently with the rest of the tour, I was not able to go on the whole of the tour. I missed out on Japan, Australia, Dubai and South Africa but managed to fly out for the visits to Washington, Hong Kong and Brussels.

One happy consequence of being at home was that I was able to receive the keys of the research centre from the builders. The date was 25 August 1997 – an historic day. All the work, all the planning, all the worries, all the dreams to have a dedicated centre for lung cancer research were now behind us. The reality was that the Roy Castle Centre for Lung Cancer Research had been completed and was now ours. It was, and remains, the only one of its kind ever built. Roy would have been very proud and we owed so much to him who made it possible for us to realise our dreams in record time. We could now get on with the bigger and more important dream of making that significant contribution to the eventual elimination of lung cancer.

****

In Washington we visited the cancer wards at the National Cancer Institute where Fiona was able to sit with and talk to sick lung cancer patients undergoing intensive chemotherapy. It is an integral part of Fiona's personality to feel deeply for anyone who is suffering or going through difficult times and she found it emotionally draining to spend time with the patients and their loved ones. She did it very bravely and, drawing on her experience during Roy's protracted illness, she somehow managed to bring them some hope and love. It took a lot out of her and I saw her break down in tears after leaving one hospital ward.

The other highlight in Washington was a reception at the British Embassy hosted by the Ambassador, Sir John Kerr. He had drawn up an extensive guest list of American businessmen and women, diplomats and charitable foundation trustees, as well as ex-patriot Britons living in the area. The Embassy is essentially a huge and beautiful home with large, majestic rooms and a magnificent garden. It was a splendid affair and I was delighted, in response to Sir John's welcoming words, to speak and tell the assembled gathering about the work of the Foundation, the research centre in Liverpool, and the purposes of the World Tour. We were all seriously jet lagged and tired but happy – nothing changed in this regard for the rest of the tour!

We had been very privileged and this type of reception would be repeated at all the stops on the tour, thanks to the great support we had received during the planning process of the tour from Baroness Lynda Chalker, a patron of the Foundation and a senior member of the House of Lords. She had considerable influence at the Foreign Office and used it to our benefit.

Next stop was Chicago for a reception at the offices of the Consul General. More speeches and more opportunities to talk about lung cancer, young people, smoking and all our other hobby horses. I left the team at the airport as they flew on to Japan and I flew back to Liverpool. The following morning I was doing an interview with long time supporter Linda McDermott on Radio Merseyside when we were connected on air to Ian Callaghan and Arthur Johnson in a bar in Tokyo. None of the team had been to bed yet, having flown with the sun ahead of the nightfall, whilst I had spent the night in an aeroplane over the Atlantic. It was a weird experience but somehow gave a real sense of the extent of world travelling done by the team from the Foundation. Incidentally, the bar from which Ian was speaking was owned by a scouser called Paul Betney and they all sounded happy and very much at home.

****

While I got on with my clinical work, making the Granada documentary and receiving the keys of the research centre, the team did their best in Japan. The feature of the visit was a presentation to several thousand members of Lions International who were holding their national convention. Sylvia addressed the convention and showed a video portraying Roy and the work of the Foundation. On the whole they didn't enjoy Japan too much. Perhaps it was the food, or they were just too tired, but they were glad when they set off again a couple of days later for Australia.

****

Sydney is a fabulous place, as I have found out recently attending my son's wedding. It's the first place I have found where I would happily have stayed forever. The view from the Opera House across the harbour towards the city is stunning and the weather is just wonderful. I am sorry now that I could not be with the team as they enjoyed a few days rest, although they still managed to get through a good deal of hard work. There was the inevitable reception with all the marvellous networking opportunities it provided. This one was hosted by the Consul General.

Wherever the tour went, Sylvia and Arthur had orchestrated numerous media opportunities with radio, television and the press. Fiona was called into action again and again and unfailingly came up with the right words, whether she was talking about smoking, patients with lung cancer, or research.

* * * * * * * * * *

I joined the team again in Hong Kong just ten days after the tour had left England. The stamina of everyone was remarkable and I was delighted to find them in good form and reasonably fresh. There was very little sightseeing; mostly it was a hard slog of continual work. Nobody shirked their responsibilities and everyone made a real effort to achieve the objectives of the tour.

We just had a couple of days in Hong Kong and, in that time, did many things. The most moving of these was a visit to a cancer ward to meet some patients with lung cancer. One of these was a relatively young man, with his wife and children by the bed. Through the doctor who acted as interpreter, Fiona spoke at length to them, without being able to change anything, but comforting them by simply being with them and sharing their suffering. The young patient spoke passionately about how smoking had given him inoperable lung cancer and the need for his government to do more. A few weeks after we left Hong Kong we learned that he had died, leaving his widow and young children as yet more victims of the scourge of tobacco and the profit makers in the tobacco industry.

On a lighter note we had a meeting in his residence with Chris Patten, the Governor of Hong Kong and spoke to him at length about our mission and aims. His positive response was helped by the presence of the FA Cup. As a boy he had been at Wembley in 1953 when his team, Blackpool FC, had played and won the Cup. For a young boy this was a thrilling experience and he could hardly believe that, all these years later, he was holding the same Cup with the name of his favourite football team engraved on the side as winners. The boy was clearly still in him, as it is in most men when they talk about their childhood sporting heroes.

We also had the privilege and experience of meeting Tung Chee Hwa, the incoming Chief Executive of Hong Kong, who would take over from Chris Patten when Hong Kong was incorporated into China a few months later by agreement with the British. Perhaps it was the fact that he was a graduate of the University of Liverpool that made him open his door and give us some of his precious time.

China has a massive problem with smoking and, in time, will inevitably have to confront a huge lung cancer epidemic. It was astonishing to sit around a small table in his office with such a powerful Chinese politician and tell him the stark truths of the present and future problems threatening his country. He was not fully aware of these and listened with interest, not being a smoker himself. I wonder if the message we gave him has remained with him and had any influence on his policies. Like so many of the influences for good generated by the Foundation, we shall probably never know.

****

I returned home from Hong Kong and, on 3 June, the team touched down in Dubai. A reception followed, hosted by the Consul General, Christopher Wilton, attended as elsewhere by local business people, doctors, scientists and charity workers. Our message was well rehearsed now but no less important for all that. Whether talking one to one, or giving interviews for the media, the team continued to hammer home the perils of smoking, the seriousness of the worldwide problem of lung cancer and the need for more research.

Fiona told the local press that she was amazed that there was not more control on the advertising of cigarettes and that people needed to be warned about what the tobacco companies were doing to them. She said that the Research Centre in Liverpool, the only one of its kind in the world, would help the people of their country as well as the rest of the world. "We have raised a subject here that has not been addressed before. Our work has been truly groundbreaking," she said.

The FA Cup continued to be very popular, especially with ex-patriots and they seemed very willing to part with their money in exchange for a picture of themselves holding the famous trophy.

****

South Africa was special and I was disappointed not to be there. Fiona visited the schools to find out more about the huge problem of smoking by young people, many of whom acquire their cigarettes for nothing, the tobacco companies being very free and easy with how they are distributed in the developing countries. Tobacco control is very weak in the Third World and tobacco promotion and advertising is rampant.

Fiona was at her best with lung cancer patients and their families, although it clearly drained her. She was able to do more of this in Cape Town, including one memorable visit to the home of a poor black South African man with advanced disease.

The highlight of the time spent in Cape Town, and perhaps of the whole tour, was a meeting with Nelson Mandela. This was arranged by Baroness Chalker and provided exceptional photo opportunities with Fiona – and, of course, the FA Cup. Mr Mandela obviously knew the significance of the Cup and held it aloft with a big smile and obvious delight. It would have been nice to have been there, and at the reception in the British High Commission, but I had my job to do back home.

He talked to all the team and listened to what they had to say. His charisma shone through and Arthur Johnson would later say, "The man is marvellous. I will never forget how he put his arms around my shoulders and said, 'Thank you for coming to see me'. It was a fabulous moment."

Now that was a memory to savour!

****

The final stop on the tour was in Brussels where I once again joined the team. This time the reception was held at the British European Embassy and was hosted by the European Ambassador Sir Christopher Wall and his wife, Lady Catherine, who had given so much support to the Foundation. It was a glittering and special occasion. Sir Christopher spoke and I responded by telling the assembled gathering about the things we feel passionately about.

The Trailblazers, the group of Merseyside Firefighters led by Peter McAdam, were also there. They had just completed their own tour around Europe climbing ladders in competition with local fire services, raising money wherever they went. It was good to see them.

We left Brussels by Eurostar the next day and arrived in London on 11 May. There was no time to stop there and we made straight for Euston Station to catch the train to Liverpool. At Euston, Fiona was asked to unveil the name of an engine just as Roy had done at Waterloo three years previously. She nearly collapsed in a heap when the name on the engine was revealed as Fiona Castle. So now there were two engines, one named after Roy and one after Fiona! Both engines then pulled us to Liverpool in the same carriages used by Roy on his tour around Britain in 1994.

****

The reception at Lime Street station in Liverpool was phenomenal. People had been kept informed throughout the tour by Arthur Johnson's reports in the *Liverpool Echo* and news items on Radio Merseyside and they turned out in their hundreds to welcome us back home. As Arthur explained, the team arrived back after more than one hundred hours of flying, the equivalent of travelling twice around the world. "Sometimes," said Arthur, "we were travelling for fourteen hours at a stretch and just got beyond tiredness. If we were occasionally weary and sick, we were all weary and sick together and propped each other up."

Tired though everyone was, they all turned up at a fundraising dinner that night at the Moat House Hotel. On the bill, along with some superb local talent, were the Supremes, Sister Sledge and the Three Degrees. Each performed separately and at the end all three groups appeared on stage together and gave one of the most exhilarating performances Liverpool can ever have seen. Even Lady Pilkington, frail though she was, was dancing in the aisles and she would have been on her table if I hadn't restrained her! A fitting end to a remarkable feat, one in which Sylvia Ingham could take special pride.

Now everyone would have to come back down to earth.

Chapter 24

Retirement – So Called!

The World Conference of the International Association for the Study of Lung Cancer took place in Dublin in August 1997. We ensured that we had a real presence there with a stand in the exhibition area and a presentation to the main conference by John Field on the Liverpool Lung Project. I was invited to address the main Board of the IASLC at their business meeting to talk about the Foundation and its activities. It must have gone down well because, at the end, several of the members of the Board asked if they would be able to apply to us for grants! Research scientists are the same the world over.

Soon after this Christine Owens and Lorna Porcellato went to Beijing for the World Conference on Tobacco and Health. Christine spoke on her role of Smoking Prevention Co-ordinator for the City of Liverpool and Lorna presented some early results of the research we were promoting in John Moores University on attitudes, perceptions and prevalence of smoking in primary schools.

These conferences further enhanced the reputation of the Foundation on the world stage and took the name Roy Castle into areas, and in a context, he could scarcely have dreamed of. Much more of this would follow in the years ahead.

****

Installation in the Centre of the specialist equipment began in September and the first scientists moved in during October. Some of them had already been working in the University but more were recruited, so that we now had a team of twenty-two dedicated scientists in epidemiology and molecular biology, working in the only purpose built lung cancer laboratory in the world.

The Liverpool Lung Project had been refined with the help of senior cancer scientists from this country and abroad and was ready to start. The aim would be to recruit 7,000 individuals from areas in Liverpool with a high incidence of lung cancer and monitor them for ten years, observing important aspects of their lifestyle and sampling at regular intervals the DNA from their lung cells coughed up in sputum. The statistical calculations were that at least 500 of these individuals would go on to develop lung cancer and the findings observed in these would form the basis of a programme for early detection and management of lung cancer. This programme, under the direction of John Field, would establish the Foundation as a major player in lung cancer research worldwide.

* * * * * * * * * *

I gave names to the various rooms and laboratories in the Centre, recognising some of those who had made a significant contribution to the establishment and development of the Foundation. Robert Powell, Sir Cliff Richard, Mildred Cooper, Lady Pilkington, Eric Morris, Eunice Salmond and others were remembered in this way.

Pride of place in the foyer of the Centre was given to a photograph of Roy, taken by Jim Connolly a couple of years before Roy contracted lung cancer. Jim is a master portrait photographer based in Liverpool and, assisted by his wife Joan, had taken countless studio pictures of celebrities and famous people. Jim told me of a conversation he had had with Roy during the sitting for the photograph during which he asked Roy how he would like to be remembered. This was long before there was any sign of Roy's cancer and, so far as anyone could predict, he had many active years in front of him. Roy's reply was something like, "Well, I'm just little old me, but I would really like to be remembered for doing something really spectacular which the whole world would notice!"

Little did he know that this wish, which he probably made tongue in cheek, would be so dramatically fulfilled.

* * * * * * * * * *

Asaf Niaz took up his position as IT Manager on 13 October. Asaf, ably assisted by Simon Critchley, has become one of the lynchpins of both the Foundation and the research programme, providing an exemplary and always cheerful service in an area which is essential but understood by very few. His only drawbacks are that he is a Manchester United supporter and has a bandit's golf handicap.

Colin Lawrence, father of Nicola Lawrence, the airline stewardess who had died from lung cancer in 1993, at the age of twenty-four, came to work in the Centre as general handyman and I was delighted to be able to maintain this contact with the family.

* * * * * * * * * *

Discussions continued with Jesme Baird about the way forward for the patient network. Jesme helped to recruit Jennifer Dickson as Patient Network Manager and the pair of them have worked together with great success since that time, complementing each other well with their different skills. With the help of patients Tom Haswell and Jim Elliot, they put together the first patient information leaflet that lung cancer patients in the UK had ever had. Entitled 'And So You've Been Told You Have Lung Cancer', it contained some stark realities. For example one chapter was entitled, 'Am I going to die?' but they insisted this was the type of information that patients wanted to have

****

For much of the year I had been planning a new campaign centred on children and smoking, inspired by the work of Tobacco Free Kids in Washington. This had always been an issue close to my heart and I wanted this to be based in a Phase 2 construction at the Centre, which would be given over entirely to exciting and original work with children. I prepared a comprehensive strategy and organisational chart which was approved by the Trustees, provided that it did not divert funds from our core activity. This condition, with which I entirely agreed, would mean that much of the plan would not be realised and Phase 2 had to be abandoned, but we did go on to make, and are still making, a significant contribution to the efforts to protect children and young people from the ravages of tobacco. A management board was formed for our work with children and held its first meeting on 11 December, 1997.

****

Trying to combine a busy surgical practice with a rapidly growing charity was difficult and at times very stressful. For some time I had been coming round to the view that one of them would have to be dropped if I was to retain my health and sanity but both were integral parts of my life and I was reluctant to give up either. I was sixty-one years old and still at the top of my powers as a surgeon. I had four good years before I had to retire and these would be amongst my highest earning years. On the other hand, the Foundation was my creation and it was my view, rightly or wrongly, that it would continue to need my input for some time to come if it was to survive and accomplish its mission. This was a crucial stage in its development and, at that time, there was no one else with the total commitment and determination to overcome all odds, whatever they might be, to realise the vision I had set out for the charity.

I knew instinctively that the Foundation would win this battle for my time but I tried to put the decision off as long as possible, not least because of the effect that retirement from surgery would have on my income and the consequences of this for my family. I might be prepared to make the sacrifice but was it fair on my wife, particularly? Fortunately, as always, Elizabeth backed me to the hilt as she has done all our married life and agreed to go along with whatever I decided was for the best.

In the second half of the year, the conflicts between my clinical work and the Foundation seemed to increase in frequency. I would be sitting in my clinic at the hospital and get a telephone call about a major problem developing, or needing a decision at the Foundation. Then I would be in London, Brussels or Glasgow on behalf of the Foundation and have to keep in touch with the hospital about my patients. It became crystal clear to me that, although I did have a certain aptitude for keeping several balls in the air at once, I could not risk the danger of harm to my patients and either I should significantly downgrade my involvement with the Foundation, or retire from my life's work of surgery. It wasn't easy.

Eventually Elizabeth and I made the joint decision that I should retire. We made this decision for the sake of the charity or, to be much more precise, for the sake of those people the charity had been set up to benefit. Other surgeons could take expert care of patients but there was no one with the vision and drive, at that stage of its development, to take the Foundation forward and ensure that it retained its integrity and unique purpose.

As soon as the decision was made I began to negotiate with the hospital authorities and we agreed that I would cease clinical work at the end of the year with an official retirement date of 31 March, 1998 the following year. In the meantime I would gradually reduce the volume of my work and hand over my patients to my colleagues. The effect of this was rapidly to ease the burdens on me and to free up my time. I would need every last minute of it in the next couple of years.

****

In October, I spent several stressful days in court defending myself against the only allegation of negligence made against me in my career. Normally, if there is anything at all in these cases, they are settled out of court to avoid all the costs involved. However, since I strenuously denied the allegation and the Liverpool Health Authority fully supported me, the case eventually arrived in court after eight distressing years of legal processes.

The problem related to a patient of mine who had died from a recognised complication after surgery. My record with this complication was amongst the best in the world and I had published my results to this effect in the world literature on several occasions. My rates were often five times better, and sometimes twenty-five times better than other surgeons, which made it particularly galling that I should be accused in this way.

I was more than relieved when the judge found in my favour, not least because I had worked all my life to establish my reputation but, just as importantly, the effect on the standing of the Foundation would have been damaging because of the high profile that I had in the community at large.

The judgment was announced, with banner headlines, fortunately positive, in the local press during the International Scientific Workshop which John Field and I had arranged at the Centre in mid-October. Attended by thirteen top level scientists from around the world, the purpose of the workshop was to examine in detail the use of technological developments in population screening and to examine the revolution which was taking place in diagnostic technology through the continued development of the biochip and the increasing number of new molecular markers for early detection of lung cancer. It also took a look at the ethical and economic implications of early detection of lung cancer, an enormous and hugely important subject in its own right. John was the brains behind the scientific content of the workshop but we were all very proud that the Foundation was making such an important contribution to international thinking and discussion. This was another of those many occasions when I would reflect on how far we have come.

* * * * * * * * * *

Soon after the workshop, with scarcely time to draw breath, we were all off to Glasgow again, this time for the official launch in Scotland of the Roy Castle Foundation, another major leap forward.

On 29 October 1997 we left Liverpool in the special train that had taken Roy around the UK three years before. Fiona was with us and the train was pulled by the two diesel locomotives which had been named after Roy and Fiona. Always looking for that extra headline, Sylvia had arranged for *Guinness Book of Records* observers to be on board as the train broke the record time for the journey between Preston and Carlisle, which includes the run over the Shap summit.

On arriving at Glasgow, we were met by a party of civic dignitaries, supported by the Strathclyde Police Pipe Band and the choir of Blackfriars Primary School. The ceremony took place over lunch in the Hunter Hall of the University of Glasgow and was hosted by Sir Graeme Davis. The Hall was full and I outlined the history of the charity and our hopes and plans for Scotland, including a proposal for a National Centre for the Lung Cancer Patient Network. In the evening, a reception and dinner dance was held in the Kelvinhall Art Gallery.

And so we were up and running in Scotland.

* * * * * * * * * *

There had been a change of government in the UK earlier in the year and the incoming Labour government appeared to be much more enthusiastic about curbing the influence of the tobacco companies and making a more determined effort to reduce the number of people smoking, including the implementation of a Bill to stop tobacco advertising.

I had been to a Tobacco Summit called by the Public Health Minister, Tessa Jowell, and was impressed by the apparent sincerity of their intentions. The Minister became a strong supporter of the Foundation and twice visited us in Liverpool. We also received a visit from the Secretary of State for Health, Frank Dobson and, on each occasion, we were able to lobby intensively for all the things we believed in.

Although we made the case very forcibly for more money for lung cancer research (in fact *any* money), this was never forthcoming and we are still waiting today. However, our voice was heard on smoking issues, particularly in relation to children whose importance, until then, no one was emphasising, preferring to focus on teenagers and young adults. We also began to campaign for the rights of lung cancer patients and here we had more success which we have been able to build on substantially over the years.

Because of what Tessa Jowell, Public Health minister, was doing to ban tobacco advertising and because of her support for the Foundation, we planned to give her a special award at our annual Awards Ceremony at the Savoy Hotel in November. However, the week before the event, I received a call in my clinic that the government was to make an exception for Formula One racing and that Tessa's husband was involved with the sport. I was asked by our staff to decide how to resolve this dilemma!

It was clear to me that it would be inappropriate to proceed, since this would discredit our awards and probably the Foundation itself. But how do you tell a Minister that you are withdrawing an award that she was due to receive at a glittering ceremony the following week? There was only one way and that was to be completely open and honest and that is what we did. She understood and remained a friend and we were able to give her a belated award the following year when the Government produced its White Paper, 'Smoking Kills'.

* * * * * * * * * *

Towards the end of the year we began to have concerns about our income. Projections suggested that we would not reach the targets set by Sylvia and her team and, although Sylvia was optimistic, everyone was asked to re-examine all their costs very closely and to manage their budgets more intensely. As David Tomkins pointed out at the Trustees' meeting, we were now in a post-building phase and there had to be a cultural change with more active and stronger cash management, a stronger focus on costs and a rethink on our income profile. We were hit by the Princess Diana Fund and the introduction of the National Lottery but, fortunately, very large sums of money continued to come in from Littlewoods Lotteries. We were, however, dangerously dependent on these.

These were the first warning signs of financial problems and falling income for the Foundation and, in retrospect, we should have been more ruthless in reducing our expenditure budgets for the following year. Each of the next few years would see us struggle to raise sufficient income to maintain our fundraising and grant expenditure.

* * * * * * * * *

On 18 December, I held my final clinic at the Cardiothoracic Centre in Liverpool. It was hard to believe that my surgical career was over as I drove out of the hospital for the last time. So many memories, so many highs and lows, so many difficulties overcome, so many patients! When I had been a young house surgeon in London, I had made a resolution that when I eventually retired, (and it seemed a long time away then), I would be in a position to look back and say that I had done what I wanted to do with my life and not taken the easy way out, whatever the challenges and obstacles I might meet on the way. Well, God had been good to me and I could be grateful for a fruitful and rewarding surgical career.

But now a new chapter was opening in my life – little did I know what lay ahead!

Chapter 25

Open at Last

There were a number of significant events in 1998, including the launch of our KATS (Kids Against Tobacco Smoke) campaign and the appointment, at last, of a new chairman of the charity; but the undoubted highlight was the official opening of the Roy Castle International Centre for Lung Cancer Research.

The year began with an important milestone when the Fag Ends team, whom we had been nurturing and supporting for several years, were incorporated into the Foundation and became Roy Castle Fag Ends. They were now officially our smoking cessation arm and we were committed to their ongoing development. Melody McGrillis, the main driving force behind the group, was now on our payroll full time, together, on a part time basis, with Wendy Feeney who had been with Mel since the formation of Fag Ends. The name Fag Ends has always intrigued people and has become a very successful brand. It originated from a competition to choose a name, which Mel and her friends had run in schools in the Breckfield area of Liverpool. Children can be very imaginative and original and their talents are not used nearly enough.

In February, Baroness Lynda Chalker hosted yet another dinner for us in the House of Lords. The main speaker this time was Robert Swan, intrepid explorer, and the only man to have walked to both the North and South Poles.

At the end of April, Fiona unveiled a statue of Roy in the exhibition room at the Centre. This had been sponsored by Norman Cowley and sculpted by Stephen Broadbent, a well known Liverpool artist. It depicted a dramatic intertwining of Roy with the Angel of the Lord, both playing their distinctive trumpets. Entitled 'The Last Trumpet', it presented a beautiful image of harmony and unity and triumphant heavenly music. It clearly enchanted Fiona and later in the year, without telling her, I arranged for a copy to be made at a greatly discounted rate and presented to her as a surprise Christmas gift from everyone at the Foundation and from everyone who had benefited from the work of the Foundation. It seemed to me a very appropriate thing to do, since, although she never looked for anything in return, this was an opportunity to repay all the huge effort and sacrifice she had made to ensure the success and development of our work, with something which would give her pleasure for many years. This gesture of mine, which I instigated in all good faith, would later receive some criticism which hurt me and which I considered to be out of place. However, in light of the criticism, I arranged for the cost to be covered by a donor and friend of the charity.

****

Huge crowds turned out for the opening of the Centre by Sir Cliff Richard on 12 May 1998. The sun shone down as they pressed up against the railings surrounding the car park. When Sir Cliff arrived, sporting a new short haircut and a healthy tan, he received a tremendous welcome and went round the whole perimeter of the railings, touching hands and saying hello to as many people as he could in the time available. There was a truly carnival atmosphere with balloons and streamers and music from the Royal Philharmonic Gospel Choir. The media were out in force, television, press and radio, to record the culmination of five years of detailed planning and huge effort to raise the funds required to build the only lung cancer research building in the whole world ...

Sir Cliff was accompanied by Robert Powell, Ken Dodd, Faith Brown, Frankie Vaughan, Jean Boht, Rick Wakeman, Lady Pilkington and, of course, Fiona Castle. Also there were Lady Betty Grantchester, John Moores, Professor Philip Love, Vice Chancellor of the University of Liverpool, Councillor Frank Prendergast, the Leader of Liverpool City Council and Dr Ruth Hussey, Director of Public Health for Liverpool Area Health Authority.

After touring the facilities in the Centre, the special guests joined nearly a hundred close friends and supporters of the Foundation in the lecture theatre for the opening ceremony performed by Sir Cliff, who said that, "Roy would have been so thrilled this has finally happened. It has been a magnificent day." Fiona said a prayer instead of a speech and I paid tribute to Roy and everyone else I could think of who had made a significant contribution to this wonderful achievement, especially Sylvia Ingham and Fiona. Lastly, after a few words by the Vice Chancellor, John Field made a short presentation on his research and Lorna Porcellato spoke about her work with children and tobacco.

Sir Cliff then went upstairs to name the 'Sir Cliff Richard Laboratories',

Frankie Vaughan named a smaller lab after the Grand Order of Water Rats, who had provided funding to equip it, and Robert Powell went to the top floor to open the 'Robert Powell Epidemiology Department'.

Everyone then departed for Anfield, home of Liverpool Football Club, to enjoy a Grand Luncheon with over 350 people from all over the country and to be entertained with a video of the history of the charity from the very beginning right up to the opening which had just taken place. The planning by Sylvia and her team was perfect.

Finally, in the evening, a Gala Dinner was held in the Moat House Hotel in Liverpool with a star studded cabaret featuring Sir Cliff, the Drifters, the Merseybeats, Ben Castle's Band and comedy from Vince Earl and Stan Boardman. Quite a day! We were all very tired but we had finally done it. Roy's heroic efforts had not been in vain.

****

In June, I was awarded a Professorship by Liverpool John Moores University, in recognition of the unique research which we were doing with young people and the ceremony was performed in the Centre by the Vice Chancellor, Professor Toyne. The title was a much appreciated honour and has proved useful in dealing with politicians, the media and overseas scientists. When I finally stepped down as Medical Director of the Foundation a couple of years later, I offered to relinquish the title but the University would not hear of it.

****

During the year, we agreed the appointment of four more lung cancer support nurses in Newcastle, Birmingham, Edinburgh and Clatterbridge at a cost of £30,000 a year per nurse, although the Edinburgh nurse was sponsored by the Bank of Scotland. This would be a significant cost to the Foundation but I felt that we had to pump money into these prime positions and demonstrate their need and effectiveness. In due course the cost would be absorbed by the NHS and eventually over three hundred lung cancer nurses would be appointed around the country, fully vindicating our pioneering actions.

****

The International Scientific Advisory Board was in Liverpool again in July and after reviewing our research programme, produced a lengthy report for the University and the Trustees. It was reassuring and supportive but made some valuable criticisms to which John Field was asked to respond. One of these was that he was diversifying too much and extending into areas which other research groups were doing and which were not essential to our unique core programme of early detection. This was particularly important in view of our limited resources and when the grants came up for renewal, appropriate action was taken.

By now John was being helped by Penny Plater who had been recruited as his PA. Penny would give eight years of outstanding service in an extremely difficult role, providing the link between scientists across Europe, America and further afield, ensuring that the most complex grant applications were accurate, complete and on time, acting as the focal point in the management of those that were successful and organising international meetings in Liverpool and elsewhere. She also looked after John's 'domestic' work in the University and, all in all, worked with an energy and attention to detail which was far beyond the call of duty.

****

The Café Royal in Regent Street, London, was the venue for the launch of our Kids Against Tobacco Smoke (KATS) on 12 June. The name had been carefully chosen to emphasise that it would be the children who would be leading the campaign and our aim was to empower the children and young people to do this and to be intimately involved in its planning and execution. This would take time but it was my conviction, which I had learned from Tobacco Free Kids in America, that the campaign would be much more effective and successful if we could achieve this.

The launch was carried out by Fiona Castle together with several youngsters who would later speak very forcefully at the conference and by Dr David Bull of BBC *Newsround* and *Blue Peter* presenter Katy Hill.

I had used all my contacts to set up a high profile conference to address the problem of young people and tobacco. Speakers included European Commissioner Padraig Flynn, Health Minister Tessa Jowell, Dr Nigel Gray, President of the International Union against Cancer, Professor Anne Charlton, Director of Health Studies at Manchester University and Clive Bates, Director of Ash. From North America came

Cliff Douglas, the lawyer who had blown the whistle on the tobacco industry in the States, and John Bloom, International Affairs Manager of Tobacco Free Kids in Washington.

All the important issues were covered, including nicotine addiction, risk taking, underachievement, tobacco marketing among young people, the role of the law and government, the importance of parental and teacher influence, the responsibility of the media, cultural influences and economic factors.

It was a high powered programme with heavyweight speakers and an appropriate starting point for KATS, which had three main objectives:

To create a social, political, legal, economic and ethical environment conducive to reducing tobacco use among children and young people

To develop and achieve public policies that support the elimination of tobacco use and exposure among children and young people

To develop a National Centre for the campaign and mobilise and strengthen support for the Centre and its objectives

These would be achieved through a twofold approach: research and politics. Research would provide the solid material on which to campaign and the politics would try to ensure the changes in government policy and law on which we campaigned. Because of the considerable political content of the campaigning arm of KATS, I wondered whether this should be based in London where there would be greater opportunities to network with other organisations and freer access to the national media. I had in mind that it would be led by a high profile Campaign Director.

KATS would evolve over time and change its shape but this was undoubtedly one of the most important initiatives to originate from the Foundation. In due course I believe that it will have a significant effect on smoking policies in this country.

* * * * * * * * * *

Towards the end of July, I met with fellow Trustees Brian Case, Rod Walker and David Tomkins, a meeting authorised by the whole Board of Trustees. The purpose of our discussions was to identify a new chairman for the charity. For a long time, perhaps even from the very beginning, I had thought that it was in the best interests of the charity for it to be led by an experienced and respected businessman or woman. Skills were required which my temperament and my training as a surgeon meant that I did not have. I had continued to hold the position because, firstly, none of the other Trustees would accept the position and, secondly, I did realise the need for leadership by someone who would maintain the vision and direction which had been set at the beginning and the best person for that, whether I liked it or not, was myself.

With the rapid expansion of the Foundation, a major capital project, very large sums of money coming in and an expanding workforce, it was now crystal clear that a change was essential and that my best role for the immediate future would be as Medical Director.

A number of names were thrown around of individuals prominent in business in the Merseyside area. I proposed Sir Philip Carter CBE, past Managing Director of the Littlewoods Organisation in its most successful days, past Chairman of the Merseyside Development Corporation which led the regeneration of Liverpool, Chairman of Governors at Liverpool John Moores University and past Chairman of Everton Football Club in its most successful period. He was a man of proven business ability and acumen, a plain speaker and clear thinker but also, more importantly, a man renowned for his integrity and good sense.

We all agreed that Sir Philip would be an ideal choice and would give the Trustees considerable confidence as we went ahead, although little did we know then what this would entail. I was delegated to go and ask him and I met him at the University on 11 September. He listened carefully as I outlined, with as much enthusiastic objectivity as I could muster, the history, aims and unique nature of the Foundation. He promised to think it over and let me know a few days later.

His response was positive and we arranged for him to meet the Trustees to talk it through with them. The interaction was good and we were all delighted and much relieved when he agreed to become our new Chairman. In our discussions I had told him that it would only require a couple of days a month of his time. I am not sure he has ever forgiven me for this because, over the next two years, he would spend hour after hour at the Centre dealing with a multitude of difficult and complex issues. Nevertheless, he has never failed to give whatever has been necessary of himself, or of his time, and he proved to be an absolute rock when the Foundation was shaken to its roots the following year.

The timing of our approach was very fortunate. Two weeks later, the current Chairman of Everton Football Club resigned, provoking a crisis and Sir Philip was once more installed as Chairman of the club with all the huge demands on his time that this involved. I have no doubt that if we had approached him two weeks later he would have said no. Someone was looking after us!

* * * * * * * * * *

For several months I had been talking to Dr Jesme Baird about the possibility of her coming to work for the Foundation. This would be a big step for her since she had a good permanent job in the cancer unit in Glasgow and was much respected there. It was clear to me, however, that her talents and personality could achieve great things for lung cancer patients and I needed real help in this part of our work. Jesme had the knowledge and the contacts to successfully promote and develop our activities with lung cancer patients and physicians. She also had excellent relations with the pharmaceutical companies and these would be key to funding some of our initiatives.

Although the Trustees were sympathetic to some extent, they were not sufficiently convinced to sanction the funding of her appointment. I was determined, however, to bring her on board, since I really believed that this was an opportunity which must not be missed and I persuaded them to allow me to take the funding from a miscellaneous budget which had been sanctioned to me for new developments during the course of the year. I agreed with Jesme that she would start working for the Foundation on 1 November 1998 and the Trustees accepted the arrangement. It was one of the best appointments I ever made.

* * * * * * * * * *

In December, the Government published its long awaited White Paper, 'Smoking Kills'. We had contributed to the thinking of parts of this, particularly the references to children. Immediately after publication, I was invited to attend a small reception in Tessa Jowell's office and was later interviewed live in the Sky News studio. It was a landmark day when an end could finally be seen to tobacco advertising in the United Kingdom.

On the darker side, we had, for the first time in our history, a deficit on our accounts. The loss was just under £300,000 and another deficit was being forecast for 1999. We were not used to this and because we had substantial reserves we were slow to react, although John O'Brien and others voiced their serious concerns and income and expenditure was rigorously scrutinised. Fundraising costs and salaries for the year remained high – in the region of £1million. This should have been severely pruned but we were persuaded to see how things went for a further year while a new fundraising drive was pursued to include our shops, a major wills and legacy campaign and development of our corporate strategy. We were naturally reluctant to cut back on our research.

＊＊＊＊＊＊＊＊＊＊

An eventful and important year, which had seen some major milestones in the history of the charity, came to an end with a sense that we were at last making real progress across the full range of our charitable objectives. We did not know what a desperate and fateful year lay ahead.

Chapter 26

Rumblings

For the first time in our history a deficit budget was set for the coming year. The Trustees were preoccupied with the finances of the Foundation throughout the ensuing twelve months and several brainstorming sessions were held to address the problems which were arising. The main worry was that fundraising income was unpredictable, although convincing presentations were made to the Trustees by individual members of the fundraising team which gave some confidence.

Against the uncertainties of fundraising income, there was the certainty of expenditure, with little room for manoeuvre on the project side (research, patient care and tobacco control) and a fear that reducing expenditure on fundraising would exacerbate the problem and result in a still higher deficit. We had large reserves which we could call on if necessary but it would be bad business to rely on these for more than a short period of time. As the year went on it began to look as if the end of year deficit would be larger than that set in the budget and this was deeply worrying. In fact, it would take several years and some radical action before we would get on top of the situation and regain a stable position.

In addition to this, there was some evidence that tensions were rising in the Fundraising Department with personal rivalries, resentments and division into camps. The magnitude and causes for this were unclear at the time but we had a far from happy team. As Trustees we should, perhaps, have stepped in at this stage, but we were at a distance from the action and not fully aware of the seriousness of the situation. No member of staff reported anything seriously amiss and, since we received regular reports in person from Sylvia Ingham, we left her to manage her team. In retrospect, I am disappointed that no one came to me to express their feelings, since I knew them all well, but perhaps they thought that I was too close to Sylvia. She did however ask Ed Stanley, one of the Trustees, to carry out the annual appraisals of her senior staff and this would bring some important matters to light which would bring things to a head towards the end of the year.

At the same time, however, many good things were happening on the medical side of the Foundation where, in contrast, we had a group of people who got on well with one another and were starting to achieve great things.

Our research team was beginning to identify the early genetic markers of lung cancer in sputum and we took delivery, courtesy of a grant for £40,000 from Astra Zeneca, of a mobile research laboratory with the facility to go out and about in the districts of Liverpool to enroll into the Liverpool Lung Project individuals at high risk of developing lung cancer. Later in the year, as budgeted, we would provide funding for the appointment of a lung cancer research fellow in the Beatson Oncology Centre in Glasgow.

The Fag Ends team was awarded a grant of £130,000 by the Merseyside Health Action Zone to extend their work across Merseyside with the employment of seven extra staff, upgrading of the telephone system and a new free telephone help line. This was vindication of the excellent work which they had been doing. To manage this increased activity and to lead our tobacco control activities, I brought Christine Owens into the Foundation from Liverpool City Council where we had been part funding her for a number of years. I again had a problem persuading the Trustees, purely on the basis of cost, but I felt that this was an essential appointment to manage our rapidly growing tobacco control activities. It was a good decision, and Christine has gone on to become an authority on all tobacco issues and has done a fine job running her team, developing new initiatives and representing the Foundation in the UK and abroad as our Director of Tobacco Control.

We were visited by Cliff Douglas, the American lawyer and tobacco expert, who had been at the forefront of many of the major legal battles fought against the tobacco companies in the United States. Other welcome visitors were Tim Jackson, Head of the Tobacco Policy Unit at the Department of Health, Dr Dawn Milner, Senior Medical Advisor of the Unit, Kevin Barron MP, Chairman of the All Party Parliamentary Group on Smoking and Ian Gibson MP, Chairman of the All Party Group on Cancer.

I tried without success to get sufficient support amongst MPs for an All Party Group for lung cancer since there was already one for breast cancer. I also wrote to the Chairman of the Parliamentary Health Select Committee inviting them to initiate an enquiry into lung cancer and to visit Liverpool. I had no success here either.

We were delighted when Buckingham Palace announced that the Royal Warrant was to be removed from cigarette packets supplied to the royal household. This was something for which we had campaigned discreetly and Fiona had written a personal letter to the Queen. After the announcement, we received a telephone call from the office of the Secretary of State for Health congratulating us on what had been achieved and the attendant press coverage was excellent.

On National No Smoking Day in March, about sixty children and teachers from Merseyside and the North of England attended a workshop at the Roy Castle Centre. The purpose was to involve them in the development of KATS and to meet and hear presentations from four teenagers from the hugely successful Florida Pilot Project. We had arranged for the American youngsters to be flown over courtesy of British Airways and we also took them up to Glasgow for some school visits and media opportunities.

At the workshop, the Florida kids really fired everyone up with their enthusiasm, ability to communicate and stories of campaigning against the tobacco companies. The challenge they threw out to people like me was to trust our young people to devise their own anti-smoking strategies and programmes and to empower them to attack, in their own way, the tobacco industry which was manipulating them. Their message to the other children at the workshop was to trust the adults who were trying to help them and not the tobacco companies who were harming them. The whole day was a huge success and the seeds were sown then of our present Anti Tobacco Youth Campaign.

In the early summer, the World Health Organisation published figures showing that lung cancer was the ninth most common cause of death in the world from all causes with nearly 1.25million cases every year. This was useful material when I went to the Labour Party Conference in Bournemouth and shared the platform with Tessa Jowell at a fringe meeting.

We received good news when Roy Morris, Chief Executive of Rathbones, agreed to become chairman of a development group to raise money for the establishment of a Roy Castle Professor of Childhood Smoking Prevention at Liverpool John Moores University. He quickly raised nearly £200,000 and persuaded the Countess of Sefton, Lady Derby to help. I wrote to Cherie Blair for support and she agreed to hold a reception at 10 Downing Street in the New Year.

Everything seemed to be going well, but the damaging turn of events within the Foundation at the end of the year brought things to a halt, although in due course we did go ahead with the Downing Street reception. The money raised by Roy was invaluable in funding developments in the primary schools research which we were already doing in the University. Roy has remained a very good and loyal friend of the Foundation.

Another good friend and supporter, Richard Faulkner, was appointed a Working Labour Peer and accepted our invitation to become a patron of the charity. His passion about the damage caused by tobacco made him a natural ally and, as Lord Faulkner of Worcester, he has campaigned vigorously on all tobacco issues, both within the House of Lords and outside. In more recent times, he has become a Trustee of the Foundation, making great efforts to attend meetings and to play an active part in the all that we do, particularly in tobacco control. He has been at the forefront of the campaign to ban smoking in public places and we have worked together especially well on this.

In September, we held the first Pause for Hope service in St Francis Xavier's church in Liverpool. This is an ecumenical initiative which I had long wanted to get started and, with the support of all the cancer charities in Merseyside, the annual event has proved to be very popular and well attended. It is aimed at all those affected in any way by cancer – patients, families, carers, professionals, administrators, politicians and scientists searching for the cure. Prayer has always been an important part of my life and, in the field of cancer, there is so much to pray about – not least that the day will quickly come when all cancers can be prevented or cured.

The following month, Dr David Dunlop, oncologist in Glasgow, became a Trustee. This was shortly before the Foundation took a serious turn for the worse and those prayers would be sorely needed.

Chapter 27

Crisis

Things came to a head towards the end of October, although for several months there had been rumblings of discontent and improper behaviour. It was to Ed Stanley that members of staff seemed to turn and he communicated his concerns to the Chairman of the Foundation, the Treasurer and the Chairman of our Employment Committee. I was left out of this loop and I still don't really know why but it may have been that I had always been so supportive of Sylvia. It was prudent also to be very discreet and take sufficient time to determine whether such serious allegations had any substance.

At a Trustees meeting on 20 October, which had been previously arranged and the purpose of which I understood to be about setting the next year's budget, the whole discussion centred on the management style of the Chief Executive and the need to restructure the Foundation. There were strong underlying tensions and much that was clearly not said so that I was confused and disturbed. Two sub-committees were set up to consider these issues further and I would be on the Restructure Committee.

Two days later, I was informed through a member of staff, whom I had no reason to distrust, of a list of allegations detailing serious areas of concern in Sylvia's execution of her role as Chief Executive. I was devastated. My training as a surgeon had not prepared me for this.

I immediately informed those Trustees I could get hold of, including the Chairman of the Employment Committee, the Treasurer and Ed Stanley. Their advice unequivocally was that the proper procedure was to inform the Chairman as soon as possible and then to arrange a meeting with Sylvia to inform her that serious allegations had been made against her and that she would be suspended until they had been fully investigated.

In fact I couldn't contact Sir Philip until the evening and, since it was Friday, we decided to hold the meeting with Sylvia first thing on Monday morning. Paula Chadwick, personal assistant to the Chairman, was present to take notes and provide a female presence. Sylvia was clearly shattered by what Sir Philip had to say. She denied that she had ever done anything to harm the charity and asked to leave the room in order to ring her family and solicitor. When she came back she informed us that she was resigning with immediate effect. She signed an appropriate letter, went down with Paula to clear some things from her office and left the Foundation. She was allowed to keep her car and mobile phone until the end of the week.

This was a tragic turn of events and sad beyond measure. Sylvia did lack a number of important management skills which, as Trustees, we should have corrected much earlier, but she had done some remarkable things and her PR and communication skills, allied with an exceptionally imaginative fundraising ability, had brought in the funds to build the research centre and had given us a national profile which we could only have dreamt about in the early years. She had also been the key in cementing the involvement of Roy and Fiona with the Foundation.

I have often asked myself, and others have asked me, if the situation could have been handled any differently but I believe that we had no alternative if we were to fulfill our responsibilities as Trustees. In fact, when we informed the Charity Commission without delay of the actions we had taken, they told us that we had "acted promptly, properly and in the best interest of the charity". We were very fortunate to have the strength and experience of Sir Philip at such a critical time. Paula Chadwick also proved to be an absolute rock during the whole of the troubled period.

Sir Philip called in external auditors to examine the Foundation from top to bottom and asked me to take control of it on a day to day basis. This was the last thing I wanted but there was no one else suitable and immediately available. I called all the staff into the lecture theatre and informed them of what had happened and, among other things, told them of my belief that the Foundation would come out of this much stronger and in much better shape. This was not wishful thinking and would eventually prove true, although it would take a couple of years to accomplish. We had exploded on to the scene as a charity and needed the discipline in our protocols, controls and management structure, which would be enforced upon us by the rigorous investigation of the Foundation which lay ahead over the next six months.

One of the first things I did was to try and unite the medical and fundraising arms of the charity, which had become increasingly separated by ill feeling and distrust. I brought Jesme Baird, Chris Owens and John Field on to the Management Executive from which they had previously been excluded. Difficulties remained, however, particularly between different factions in fundraising and I was to have a continual stream of members of staff at my doors with complaints and problems of one kind or another.

It was an increasingly stressful time with investigating auditors, unsettled staff, intense media interest and discussions with the Charity Commission. The Trustees were also divided, with suspicions of individual agendas. The Foundation was literally fighting for survival, particularly as the crisis had come at a time when we had already become concerned about our financial position.

Fiona had just about remained on board but was very troubled by the recent chain of events. She disliked the bad publicity which had been generated and found this very difficult to accept. She also felt that Sylvia's good work far outweighed any wrong she might have done and that the situation had been mismanaged by the Trustees. We tried to persuade her otherwise but without success. She continued to support the Foundation but it was clear that her heart was torn and she felt very deeply for the distress that Sylvia was experiencing.

No one, including myself, was spared a detailed examination, firstly by the external auditors and then by the Charity Commission, which carried out a full investigation of the charity including not only the allegations raised against Sylvia Ingham, but also the role of the Trustees in the running of the charity as a whole and the internal controls and procedures used by the Foundation in the management of its business.

Numerous lengthy meetings of the Trustees were held, often lasting five hours at a time. As well as addressing all the difficulties raised by the continuing crisis, we had a charity to run and important decisions to make. We decided to go ahead with two major fundraising projects, Sir Cliff Richard's 60th Birthday Party in September 2000, which Sylvia had secured, and Quest for the Cure, another ambitious international tour planned by Sylvia for the summer of 2000, this time to the United States.

Financial concerns were exacerbated by the extensive negative publicity. It looked as if we would have to plan for another deficit in 2000 and I had to negotiate with John Field a reduction of £300,000 in the research budget.

But the decision which caused me most distress was made by the Trustees to close the Glasgow office and all the patient care activity managed from there, if this would result in significant savings. I had initiated this activity and it was close to my heart. To discontinue it would have serious implications for the Foundation, not least in the additional bad publicity it would generate. At the end of the day, however, the economics of the situation carried too much weight with the Trustees and a decision was made to examine the savings and report further to the Restructure Committee on 22 December when the final decision would be made. I felt that I should inform Jesme Baird about this and did so after the meeting. I found it very difficult and, not surprisingly, she was very angry and distressed.

When challenged, Jesme can be very formidable and she set to work to disprove the figures which had been set before the Trustees and to demonstrate that some of the funds held by the Foundation had been specifically donated for the patient care activities, information which had not been made available to the Trustees. In a letter to the Trustees she vigorously reiterated the view that the bad publicity generated would be catastrophic for the Foundation, particularly in medical circles, and indicated in forceful terms that the patient care division could and should be run for a further twelve months at least.

The Restructure Committee re-examined the figures with the Finance Director in the light of what Jesme had said and agreed to allow patient care to continue for six months, after which it would be expected to be self funding. Jesme had saved the day and should take every credit for this. I was given the task of extracting more savings from John Field and of persuading the relevant health authorities to take over the costs of employing our nurses.

The next day – two days before Christmas – I cracked. Trying to keep everyone together had been a nightmare and had brought me to the verge of a nervous breakdown. Physically and mentally exhausted, I was completely drained after two months of constant strain, day and night. I had dealt with hundreds of problems, many of them very complex – investigating auditors, charity commissioners, the media, Fiona, staff anxieties and resentments to one another, patrons and corporate contacts, Trustees, Sir Cliff Richard, Glasgow, budgets, the Downing Street reception, Quest for the Cure, etc, etc.

During the morning, after several near things, I finally broke down in tears and couldn't stop. I suppose I felt everything so deeply and personally because of my passionate belief in the Foundation and what it was trying to do. Christmas proved to be a difficult time but, as always, my wife, Elizabeth, was there with precious comfort and support.

The Trustees had agreed in mid-December to search for an acting Chief Executive but had, as yet, had no success. For me this couldn't come quickly enough and I prayed long and hard, not just for myself but for everyone involved in this sorry mess.

Interestingly, though, it never occurred to me to give up.

Chapter 28

Checks and Balances

The new millennium began with a telephone call from Peter Say on 5 January. Peter had known the Foundation for a number of years having worked for Coca Cola at the height of their support for the charity. He rang to reassure me of his continuing support and that recent events would make no difference.

This was agreeable enough but, during the conversation, I mentioned that we were looking for an acting Chief Executive. He told me of an old colleague of his who had just retired from a senior management position at Cadbury Schweppes and who might be suitable. His name was Roger Evans and Peter agreed to sound him out.

A few days later I spoke to Roger and arranged for him to come over for an interview. We took care to get approval from the Charity Commission and within a week he had started. It was as if an enormous load had been lifted off my shoulders and I have felt the benefit ever since. Roger drew upon his extensive management experience and his undoubted interpersonal skills to guide the Foundation through the next two years so that, when he left, the Foundation was very much strengthened and able to refocus on its important mission.

Lorraine O'Brien followed Roger into the Foundation as Head of Fundraising with a background in marketing and newspapers. She worked immensely hard to keep the money coming in and oversaw the successful completion of Quest for the Cure and the Sir Cliff Richard 60th birthday party. Her media experience was invaluable in the aftermath of Sylvia's resignation and the conduct of the Charity Commission enquiry.

Fiona remained up and down, anxious about the reputation of the charity which bore her husband's name and deeply concerned about the traumas being experienced by Sylvia Ingham. She did not want to make any decision about her relationship with the Foundation until after the Charity Commission report was published but eventually, some months later and following mediation by the Bishop of Liverpool, it was agreed that she would draw back from the charity. This was very sad since I have always hoped that Fiona and her family would take great pleasure and pride in what has been achieved in Roy's name, not only in the UK but around the world. I am still optimistic that one day her position will be restored.

The Charity Commission report was published in May 2000 and found that Sylvia's conduct had fallen below the standard reasonably to be expected of the Chief Executive of a charity. They regarded it as an acceptable resolution that she had agreed to reimburse the charity for any non-business expenditure.

I was criticised for having approved the purchase of a statue of Roy for Fiona, although it was recognised that I had done this in good faith, that there had been no benefit to myself, and that subsequently I had found a benefactor to cover the cost of the sculpture.

The Trustees were criticised for having failed to exercise proper oversight and scrutiny in a number of aspects of the Foundation's operational management and, consequently, there had been insufficient attention to effective systems of management and control, including the activities of the Chief Executive.

In mitigation, it found that the charity had grown very quickly as an organisation from its original structure and Sylvia's fundraising skills had succeeded in raising significant amounts of money in a relatively short period, which had allowed the charity to develop its core activities such as the research centre, patient care and tobacco control.

The rapid growth, it said, was not accompanied by a sufficiently supportive management culture and robust checks and balances, so that some poor practice developed and appeared to go unchallenged.

The report set out a number of recommendations and proposals designed to provide a clear framework of effective systems for managing the Foundation's business and resources. These included governance, finance and control systems, management and human resource issues and fundraising.

Roger Evans began immediately to work with the Trustees to implement these recommendations and proposals and was sufficiently successful in this as to satisfy completely the Charity Commission's officers, who kept the charity under close review for a full year after their report. There is no doubt that, in terms of governance, controls and management structure and procedures, the Foundation came through its trials infinitely strengthened and that Roger Evans did a superb job in achieving this.

Following the earthquake associated with Sylvia's resignation there were a number of aftershocks, which were highlighted in the media over the next eighteen months, but they finally died down and we were able once more to concentrate on the pursuit of our charitable objectives.

Public statements of continued support from Sir Cliff Richard and Robert Powell gave us all a huge lift.

Chapter 29

Back to Business

A reception at 10 Downing Street, another at the White House, a major conference in Washington and Sir Cliff's 60th Birthday party – all proved that there really was life after all our troubles. Nevertheless, we had to work very hard and every now and then a media story would erupt, usually instigated by someone who had a grievance against the Foundation. We dealt with them honestly, one by one, and eventually they would stop altogether.

Sylvia Ingham took us to an industrial tribunal for unfair dismissal but we settled this before it came to court in order to avoid days of high profile negative publicity for the Foundation. Sylvia had resigned and had not received three months severance pay to which she was probably entitled and the Trustees decided to pay her the balance of this after deducting a sum agreed with her lawyers for repayment of money she owed to the Foundation. Sylvia withdrew her claim and that was the end of the matter.

On 24 February 2000 we had the enormous privilege of a reception at 10 Downing Street to raise money for our Kids Against Tobacco Smoke campaign. This was hosted by Cherie Blair and attended by about forty people, some of whom had flown over from the United States. It had not been easy drawing up a guest list for such a prestigious event and we had to be quite ruthless in our selection. My wife, naturally, would love to have been there but there just wasn't room and it was only right that priority should be given to others who could help the Foundation financially.

Cherie Blair was charming and gracious when she spoke and I have to admit to being intensely nervous, to the extent that I had great difficulty remembering the punch line of a light hearted joke which I have used hundreds of times to get things off to a happy start and encourage the audience to listen to the rest of what I have to say!

We all felt the same thrill going through the famous doors and up the staircase to the receptions rooms where we were free to wander around and view the seventeenth century furniture and paintings and to talk informally about the work of the Foundation. It was a wonderful experience and we cemented relationships which would later bear much fruit.

Soon after this I decided to step down as Medical Director of the Foundation. I was worn out by the events of the last few months but I also genuinely felt that it was the right time to hand over to younger people who, as dedicated professionals and experts in their respective fields, could now be given their heads and prove their worth. It had always been my intention from the very beginning to find good quality individuals who could take responsibility for the different areas of the Foundation's activities.

In John Field, Jesme Baird and Christine Owens I believed that we now had those people for research, patient care and tobacco control and subsequent events have proved me right. From now on my role would be to maintain intact the vision with which we had started out, to encourage and assist as much as possible by drawing on my considerable experience and by speaking out in the media on behalf of the Foundation when appropriate. I would also have a useful role in motivating potential donors and corporate collaborators to help us in our work.

It was the end of an era but I have seen a few of those in my time.

****

On 6 June 2000, the Foundation announced a three year partnership with one of the world's leading biotechnology companies, Incyte Genomics Inc, based in the USA. As John Field explained, by working together, applying the strengths of both organisations, the partnership would use state-of-the-art, industrial scale, high throughput, biotechnology to derive new knowledge about which genes are damaged in lung cancer. This new knowledge would allow us to tackle directly these damaged genes and interrupt the process of lung cancer development.

At about this time our external UK Grants Committee met to carry out an in-depth review of our research programme. Their detailed report to the Trustees was most encouraging. In addition to some constructive criticism they stated that overall they were very impressed with the work being carried out and described it as "groundbreaking and unique", not only in the UK but also worldwide and, in their opinion, the Liverpool Lung Project was our "jewel in the crown". They particularly complimented the work of Dr Lakis Ligliou who had produced many high ranking publications and was recognised internationally at a number of European and North American meetings.

****

In June, we were off to America again, this time as part of our Quest for the Cure, a dramatic title, but an important educational, fundraising and awareness campaign initiated by Sylvia Ingham before she left the Foundation. Responsibility for seeing it through fell to Lorraine O'Brien and what a great job she did!

On 22 June, after months of detailed panning, over eighty people, including eleven teenagers, left Manchester Airport to learn how lung cancer is managed in the United States and how the issue of youth smoking is tackled there. The idea was that they would return home much better informed about these matters and become effective advocates of the Foundation among their work colleagues and social contacts.

High point of the Quest would be a reception at the White House where the young people with us would sign a joint declaration with their American counterparts and together receive letters of support from the President of the United States and the Prime Minister of Great Britain. Negotiations were still taking place with NASA to take the signed joint declaration up to the International Space Station, where it would be hung as a declaration from the young people of the world for the new millennium.

Teams of four came from many of the UK's leading companies, including Littlewoods, Asda, KPMG, Barclays bank, Rolls Royce, British Airways, QVC, Rathbones and Barclaycard. There was also a very lively team from John Moores University. Each team had raised a considerable amount of money in the year leading up to the Quest and we were hopeful that they would continue to do so after their return.

I had gone out a couple of days earlier with John Field and Christine Owens to speak at a scientific conference at the National Cancer Institute in Washington. This was a unique conference, co-hosted by the Roy Castle Foundation and the Cancer Research Foundation of America and sponsored by Bristol Meyers Squibb. The twin themes of the conference, attended by over one hundred scientists, were the early detection of lung cancer and the protection of children from tobacco exposure.

John Field told the delegates about our research, Christine Owens highlighted our work with children and I gave an overview of the history and work of the Foundation. The rest of the day was taken up with some very high powered scientific presentations and discussions and we felt very proud to have had a major part in putting such a conference together in the US capital city. Time and again I have been amazed at how far we have come as a charity and this was another such occasion.

The rest of the Questers arrived in Washington later that day and just about had time to wash and change before setting off for the British Embassy for a reception hosted by the Ambassador, Sir Christopher Meyer. In attendance were a large number of businessmen and women, politicians, pharmaceutical company executives, US charity workers and some of the scientists who had previously attended the symposium at the National Cancer Institute.

In his speech of welcome, Sir Christopher handed over the letter of support from the Prime Minister "for this important initiative which highlights the responsibility of the governments of the world to give high priority to the health and wellbeing of our children".

Rhys Morris from Wales had been chosen as the spokesman for the young Questers and he responded to the Ambassador with a passionate few words. Rhys, aged sixteen, had lost his father to lung cancer at the age of thirty-eight and it was very moving to listen to him. In my reply, I spoke about the purpose of Quest for the Cure and the seriousness of the problem of youth smoking worldwide.

Rhys was in action again the following day at a reception in the Indian Treaty Room at the White House. In the presence of the Director of the National Cancer Institute representing the President, Rhys and Chelsea Richmond, leader of the US youth delegation, read out the signed messages of support from Bill Clinton and Tony Blair and jointly signed the following declaration on behalf of the children of the world:

As we enter the new Millennium we are confronted by the fact that 250 million children alive in the world today will die from a smoking related disease.

We call upon governments everywhere to turn this epidemic around. We do not want to grow up in a world where millions of us will suffer and many die prematurely as a result of smoking tobacco.

We plead with you to meet your responsibilities towards us, the children of the world, and to use all your power and authority to protect us from the harmful effects of tobacco.

After signing the declaration, Rhys said, "Thank you, Mr President and Mr Prime Minister for your letters of support, which are very encouraging. Please do everything you can to give me and my friends everywhere a long and healthy life."

It was a powerful occasion and I summed up by saying, "This proclamation from the youth of Great Britain and America sends a loud and clear message to governments all over the world. It will serve as a beacon of hope for this and future generations of our children, that those with responsibility for their welfare will protect them from the ravages of tobacco."

We took the declaration to Florida a few days later, where it was received at NASA by Dr Wycliffe in the Rocket Garden at the Kennedy Space Centre, from where it would be flown to the International Space Centre when *STS 106 Atlantis* blasted off later in the year.

The White House reception was followed by a teen tobacco summit at the headquarters of the Campaign for Tobacco Free Kids. Attending this were our young Questers and a selected group of American teenagers who had been active in fighting tobacco use. The purpose was to exchange ideas and tactics in their respective countries and it was a lively event.

"Youth advocates are one of the strongest weapons we have to fight youth tobacco both nationally as well as in local schools and communities," said Mathew L Myers, President of Tobacco Free Kids.

He was preaching to the converted.

During the night, after the White House reception, one of the Questers received news that her son had been killed in a car accident in Liverpool. This was absolutely devastating and she had to return immediately to England. The rest of us were getting ready to leave for the airport when we were told and it was deeply upsetting.

The next leg of the tour was in Tampa, Florida, where we spent two days visiting the H Lee Moffitt Cancer Centre at the invitation of the Director, Dr Jack Ruskdeschel. The whole group toured the state of the art facilities at this prestigious cancer research and treatment centre and was given a series of presentations by doctors, surgeons and oncologists on how lung cancer was managed at this institution where success rates were triple those in the United Kingdom, as is the case throughout North America. The Questers learned an enormous amount about lung cancer and the questions they asked demonstrated a significant level of understanding.

Our scientists in Liverpool had been working in collaboration with those at the H Lee Moffitt Cancer Centre for four years and, at a special dinner hosted by the Moffitt Centre, Dr Ruskdeschel and I signed a Twinning Agreement to continue to work together on all issues concerned with lung cancer and plaques were exchanged to mark the event.

Our next stop was Orlando for the tour of NASA and the handover of the Declaration signed in the White House as well as a visit to Disney Celebration Hospital for a sit down lunch with speeches and more education on the lung cancer wards and investigation units. Naturally we also went to Disney World which was an eye opener for me since I had always thought of it as being completely child orientated. I was completely fascinated by the scientific theme park, Epcot.

We arrived back in Liverpool on 3 July to yet another fundraising party at the Moat House Hotel. The Questers had had a lot of fun and learned so much about lung cancer. We had raised awareness of lung cancer and of the Foundation, hosted an important scientific meeting, developed new partnerships and highlighted in spectacular fashion the issue of young people and tobacco. Lorraine and her team had done an amazing job in getting so many people around America on such an eventful trip.

****

Soon after we got back we received the sad news from Sunderland that Lynn Kish had lost her battle against small cell lung cancer. Lynn was one of those who had never smoked and she left behind her husband and two small children, Carl and Jack. A bright and bubbly personality, she loved to sing and entertain in her spare time and perhaps she suffered, like Roy Castle, from the effects of passive smoking. There were other similarities to Roy in that, even when she lost all her hair as a result of intense and debilitating chemotherapy, she maintained her spirits and displayed a cheerfulness and bravery which impressed us all immensely. She continued to sing and give enjoyment to others but now she was also doing it to raise money for the Foundation.

The example given by Lynn, and by so many other cancer patients who help this and other charities, is overwhelming and I was very pleased when her family asked me to speak at her funeral. Since she died, her colleagues at the Royal and Sun Alliance centre in Sunderland have continued to raise funds for us and a photograph of Lynn and a tribute to her hangs in the Roy Castle Centre so that she will never be forgotten. It also serves as a reminder of all those other lung cancer patients who have helped us over the years.

As the year went on we were worried about the performance of our fourteen charity shops, some of which did well but the operation as a whole, which we had established as a separate trading company, was losing money. We had invested a considerable sum in the shops at the beginning and the Charity Commission, from whom we took advice, was adamant that we should invest no more. We put in place a new management team, superbly led by Pat Tisdale, and a schedule for repayment of some of the money invested but the retail sector was undergoing something of a revolution, with intense competition in the high street clothing market and all charity shops were feeling the brunt of this competition.

We developed a recovery plan to reduce our cost base, close the unprofitable shops, reduce and slim down the head office running costs and manage stock control more efficiently. It would take a year or two for these measures to take effect and we had to transfer the leases on most of our shops outside the North West of England to the Marie Curie Cancer Care organisation.

****

A constant pattern was emerging, which had first shown itself after completion of the Roy Castle Centre in 1998 and which persists to this day. The project side of the Foundation – research, patient care and tobacco control – has been consistently successful and continues to develop in a remarkable and sustained way. But lung cancer has no attractive features and few survivors to plead its cause, so that raising the funds to allow the work to be done has been consistently difficult. Apart from the years when Roy was with us, and in the first few years after his death, fundraising has lagged significantly behind the levels required to allow us to progress at the pace required to match the ability of those we fund. In order for them to reach their potential in the battle to defeat lung cancer, we need the help of either the government, or one of the major cancer charities but, sadly, neither has so far been forthcoming. In the meantime, we will do our best but we could do so much more with the right amount of funding.

We finished the year with another deficit, the third in a row from 1998, and a further significant drain on our reserves. Bold action would be needed if we were to survive.

Chapter 30

Benefits and Deficits

As we went into 2001 we were heartened by the appointment of three new Patrons, Dame Judi Dench, an international star whose husband, Michael Williams, had recently died of lung cancer, Melanie Chisholm (Mel C from the Spice Girls), and Alan Hansen, past captain of Liverpool Football Club and prominent television pundit. All three, in very different ways, would give the Foundation their commitment and invaluable support.

Jim Couton, recently retired Vice President of Coca Cola Enterprises UK, became a Trustee, bringing extensive management experience and a lot of good humour to our deliberations. John Moores stepped down as President of the Foundation and I was asked to take his place. This gave me the role in which I could best serve the Foundation. As Jack of all trades and master of none I could, when asked, give every section of the charity the benefit of my experience, encourage and cultivate supporters of all kinds, help when appropriate with the media and, most of all I could ensure that our mission remained intact and that we did not lose sight of the urgency of our task.

****

One of our stated objectives at the very outset of the charity was to raise awareness of the seriousness of the problem of lung cancer and of its high incidence, heavy mortality, lack of research and inadequate clinical resources. We had made a lot of headway in achieving this over the years but much remained to be done.

Jesme Baird, who by now held the title of Director of Patient Care, took this in hand and, with the help of Dr David Dunlop, organised a Lung Cancer Awareness day in February 2001. A panel discussion by prominent cancer specialists was held in Church House, Westminster, followed by a media conference. The purpose was to expose the inadequacies and inequalities in lung cancer research, diagnosis and care and to campaign for these to be overcome. The impact through television, press and radio was considerable.

This encouraged Jesme and others to plan a Lung Cancer Awareness month for November to coincide with that already held for a number of years in the USA by ALCASE (Alliance for Lung Cancer Advocacy Support and Education) and which together they would develop into an international yearly event. Macmillan Cancer Relief became close partners with us in promoting this within the UK.

Also on the international front, Jesme, on behalf of the Foundation, became a prime mover in the establishment of the Global Lung Cancer Coalition, an association of lung cancer organisations around the world, formed to promote the interests of lung cancer patients worldwide and to campaign on all the issues dear to our heart. Their stated objective was, 'To promote global understanding of the burden of lung cancer and the rights of patients to effective early detection, better treatment and supportive care, to raise awareness and to de-stigmatise the disease.' The founding sponsor was Astra Zeneca and members included Spain, France, Germany, Japan, Italy, the United States and the United Kingdom. Many more would follow.

At a later date we were awarded, in the face of stiff competition from America and Japan, the secretariat of the GLCC to run this international body from our office in Glasgow.

* * * * * * * * * *

During the summer nearly one hundred cancer scientists attended three consecutive international conferences on early detection of lung cancer at the Roy Castle Centre in Liverpool. Firstly the International Scientific Advisory Board met to review our research and this was immediately followed by a three day workshop to exchange information and ideas on state-of-the-art research and diagnostic techniques as well as some of the ethical issues associated with population based research. Finally, another workshop followed, sponsored by the American Cancer Society and the National Cancer Institute in Washington, during which doctors and scientists from Europe and the United States discussed setting up a joint research project into the use of spiral CT scanning in the detection of early lung tumours.

The fact that three such important conferences could be held consecutively in the Roy Castle Centre demonstrated clearly the leading role which the Foundation was playing in international lung cancer research.

* * * * * * * * * *

Cartoon Network, the children's satellite television channel, teamed up with us for De-feet Lung Cancer Day, a schools fundraising initiative first proposed by Morag McIntosh when she was our head of fundraising in Glasgow. The idea was for children to go into school wearing funny shoes and give a pound to the Foundation, in return for which the Foundation would give the school materials and help in smoking prevention. For a full week prior to the event Cartoon Network allowed its main cartoon characters to wear funny shoes of one kind or another and messages would be broadcast between programmes.

****

"It's always satisfying to receive an award but this is special." This was Sir Cliff Richard speaking after the laboratory named after him in the Roy Castle Research Centre won the Best Laboratory in the UK Award at the Laboratory News Industry Awards for 2001.

The lab was judged on design, security, safety, IT provision and support, space, light, environment, storage, location and state-of-the-art equipment and facilities, quite a formidable list of criteria for the first purpose built facility to undertake lung cancer research.

"From the outset I was thrilled to have my name linked to the laboratory," continued Sir Cliff, "particularly as its work into lung cancer was really pioneering. Now I'm proud and delighted that 'my' laboratory has won such prestigious recognition. It reflects wonderfully on the research team and the charity as a whole." I made the point that we should not forget the many friends and supporters of the Foundation who contributed the funds to make this possible.

****

In September, we held the first ever National Lung Cancer Patients' Conference. A few years earlier I had attended in Washington a conference organised by ALCASE which linked patients with doctors, scientists and administrators using satellite communications. The power of patients and the strength of their advocacy became clear to me then and I resolved to organise a meeting in the UK in which the patients and their families would be at the centre of proceedings, giving them a public forum to campaign for more research and fairer allocation of resources. I envisaged a major meeting in London at which Ministers and others in public office would be invited to attend and listen to those directly affected by the disease making their case. Appropriate celebrities would also be invited to take part and the media would be given the opportunity to highlight selected campaign issues.

I stepped down before I could do any of this and, in any case, we probably would not have been able to afford it but Jesme Baird and our Patient Care team took up the baton and organised in Liverpool a very successful Patients' Conference attended by nearly one hundred delegates from all over the country. Several powerful patient advocates emerged from that conference and ensuing ones and we now provide media training for those who are willing to put themselves forward.

****

We had had a very successful year in developing our charitable objectives but yet again we finished with a deficit on our accounts, this time just over £300,000. We couldn't go on like this. What was to be done?

Chapter 31

Hanging in the Balance

For the next eighteen months the Foundation's financial condition gave rise to increasing concern. Our team of fundraisers worked hard and had some success but it was never enough to meet the demands we had put upon ourselves in research, patient care and tobacco control. The consistent problem of success in pursuing our charitable objectives and inability to finance current activity, never mind take it to a higher level, dogged us every day, with no relief in sight from government or other sources. We had made great progress in addressing one of the most serious public health problems facing the nation, but it seemed that we would have to do it on our own.

In view of this it was ironic, though another huge achievement, that, at this time, our research team won a large grant from the European Union worth 3 million euros to direct and manage an early detection research programme in twelve academic centres across ten European countries. The grant was indicative of the quality of our scientists and the work which they were doing but was for a new project, additional to what we were already doing, and did not help our money problems.

Also on the positive front, Jesme Baird was invited to chair the NICE (National Institute for Clinical Excellence) committee which was charged by the government with setting clinical guidelines for the treatment of lung cancer in the National Health Service. The government would also set up a national Lung Cancer Advisory Group and Jesme and Terry Kavanagh, who by now had survived surgery for lung cancer for twelve years, were appointed to it.

The government also established a virtual National Cancer Research Institute, a coalition of major cancer charities, with the aim of co-ordinating research at national level and we were invited to become members. Altogether it seemed that, at last, we were meriting proper recognition and beginning to exert some real influence.

* * * * * * * * * *

In their report of May 2002, following an inspection to review the progress we had made since their investigation two years previously, the Charity Commission found that:

The charity had succeeded in making extensive changes in four key areas: governance, finance and control systems, management and human resources issues, and fundraising. It would not have been possible for the charity to have made these improvements without the drive of the Board and the active management by senior staff. The charity is run in a professional, well organised and controlled way, underpinned by the commitment and enthusiasm of the staff. There are many examples of good practice noted.

At last we had a clean bill of health and, in many ways, were now a model charity. Roger Evans, as Chief Executive, had worked tirelessly and through many difficulties to achieve this, with the full support of the Trustees and staff of the Foundation.

****

Roger's main work was now done and he announced that he would be leaving at the end of August. The search began immediately for a successor, for someone who could build on his achievements and secure the financial future of the Foundation whilst maintaining and even enhancing the remarkable progress made in pursuing our charitable objectives. It was a big task and would take a big man or woman to do it. We had a solid base of organisation and medical achievement but the outlook was grim if we could not further cut our costs and increase our income.

Mike Unger was appointed to the job, commencing 1 September 2002. Mike had that rare combination of a soft heart and ruthless efficiency and determination. He had been editor of both the *Liverpool Echo* and the *Liverpool Daily Post* before becoming editor of the *Manchester Evening News*, the largest regional newspaper in the country. He held this post for fourteen years during turbulent times, including the Stalker drama and subsequent inquiry. He had served on the main Board of the Guardian Media Group plc and was well known in business and social circles. His experience of business and the media gave him an excellent background for his new position with the Foundation. He would, most importantly, prove to be the pivotal figure in rescuing the Foundation from the threat of insolvency.

It didn't take Mike long to develop a deep understanding of the mission and purpose of the Foundation and he immediately addressed our fundraising strategy, which was still too reliant on the unpredictable income from events. Some staff were allowed to leave and others reorganised to give greater emphasis to legacies, trusts, in memoriam donations and corporate partnerships, all of which could be progressively built up until they produced a steady and predictable income.

Such a strategy would take time, perhaps several years, to come to fruition and in the meantime we had the immediate perilous financial position of the Foundation to correct.

Several options were open to the Trustees including merging with another charity or partnership with the University or a pharmaceutical company such as Astra Zeneca, which we understood was looking for new research laboratories and had a keen interest in lung cancer.

The Trustees decided to set up a subcommittee to consider the future of the Foundation with the premise that a stand alone charity was not an option and that the charity would have to be wound up by 28 February 2003 if a strategic solution to our financial difficulties could not be found. I was extremely upset to be excluded from this subcommittee, particularly as the reason given was that I was "too emotional to be objective". I thought this was complete nonsense, since I had spent a lifetime making difficult objective decisions in the highly emotional environment of cancer surgery. Yes, I feel deeply about the Foundation, or more accurately about the people the Foundation was formed to help, but I have always been able to see the need for decisive action when required and have never been afraid to take such action, whatever the consequences.

The Trustees knew that I would fight hard to preserve the integrity and independence of the Foundation since I felt that loss of this independence, such as could result from merger with another charity, would result in lung cancer falling once again in the list of priorities and we would be back to where we were before we raised the profile of this Cinderella cancer.

Nevertheless, I had held discussions, in the aftermath of the Sylvia Ingham resignation, with Professor Gordon McVie, Director General of the Cancer Research Campaign, in which he said to me, "If you want to become the lung cancer arm of the Cancer Research Campaign, let's talk". He admitted that they had 'a big hole' in lung cancer research and did come to talk to the Trustees, but we did not have sufficient confidence in what was being proposed and decided to carry on as we were. Such a merger would be better done from a position of strength rather than of weakness if we were to be able to protect our mission.

The conclusions of the subcommittee confirmed the premise on which it had been formed and Mike Unger was charged with approaching other charities, the University of Liverpool and Astra Zeneca with a view to a takeover, or merger, with any one of these.

****

George Harrison died on 29 November. Coming from Liverpool, as he did, and dying of lung cancer, I tried everything I could to contact his family to ask them to help the Foundation. I contacted his surgeon, his agent, Sir George Martin, who had worked so closely with him, and anyone else we could think of, but without success. Perhaps one day we will be able to do something with his family and fans to preserve his memory in a way which helps all those who may suffer from the disease which prematurely took his life.

The list of other famous people who have died from lung cancer is remarkable. John Wayne, Yul Brynner, Walt Disney, Jack Benny, Gary Cooper, George Peppard, Groucho Marx, Betty Grable, Humphrey Bogart, King George VI, Louis Armstrong, Michael Williams, Nat King Cole and Vincent Price.

Just a little from the estate of any of these, or from their families or fans, would enable us to do so much.

****

Mike Unger began confidential discussions with a number of organisations and a potential miracle slowly emerged. The University of Liverpool had long been criticised at a national level for the lack of co-ordination and investment in its various cancer research programmes and it was felt that this had inhibited the attraction to Liverpool by the University of the highest calibre of research scientists and associated grant funding.

A review had been carried out by the University over the last two years and, in fact, I had taken part in this (some of the meetings had been held in the Roy Castle Centre). A decision had only recently been taken by the new Vice Chancellor and the new Dean of Medicine to establish a Centre of Excellence for Cancer Research in the University, with the appointment of two new professors of the highest quality, together with their back up teams. The Roy Castle Centre, with its state-of-the-art facilities and proximity to the University, would make an ideal location for such a centre. They therefore expressed to Mike an interest in purchasing the building.

I had no objection at all to this, provided we retained our independence as a charity and continued to operate all our activities from the Centre. I hoped also that the Centre would retain the Roy Castle name since many thousands of people had contributed to the cost of the building because of their admiration and love for Roy. Such an arrangement would have considerable benefits to the Foundation. In addition to the large sum of money received for the sale of the building, we would be relieved of all the running costs, (maintenance, repair, insurance, heating, lighting etc), which were such an enormous drain on our resources year after year.

It might be asked why we had not gone down this path before the Centre was built but, in fact, the University had no interest in doing this in 1995, nor did they have any money at that time to finance it. Quite simply, if we had not gone ahead and built the Centre it would never have been built and the opportunity would not now have been there for the University to acquire such a magnificent facility.

As we went through the process in December of setting our budgets for 2003, there was no guarantee at all that the deal with the University would go through and, in the meantime, the clock was ticking away towards 28 February, after which it had been decided we would have to call in the receivers if no solution to our financial problems was found.

Chapter 32

Back on Course

The letter came on 21 February, just three days before the specially arranged Trustees meeting to determine whether the Foundation could continue. The University confirmed that they would purchase the building and we all breathed a collective sigh of relief. The details of the deal had to be worked out but the future of the charity was secured.

Mike Unger had found a way through the minefield of University politics and managed to overcome one difficulty after another. He had been greatly assisted at Trustee level by Graham Morris and by Paula Chadwick who, as always, beavered away behind the scenes, advising, helping and collating all the various strands of what were very complex negotiations and, not infrequently, politely knocking a few heads together.

The deal, which was eventually signed on 1 August 2003, allowed the Foundation to retain its independence and to continue all its activities as before, though moving en masse to the top floor of the building. It was decided that the Roy Castle name would be retained on the building and the University wrote to Fiona for her agreement.

Overriding all of this was the fact that the University gave us a substantial sum of money, several million pounds, which, when added to the savings made by the Foundation in not having to maintain and service the building, would guarantee our financial security for the foreseeable future.

We recognised that we had sold the family silver and would not be able to do this again. It was imperative, therefore, to develop and implement a new strategy for the Foundation, particularly in the area of fundraising, and this was done.

****

Life went on and we were back in the House of Lords on 19 March for the launch of a teaching pack for primary schools, entitled *World of Tobacco*. This was developed in association with TACADE, a charity experienced in producing and distributing this type of material and was based on the research we had been funding in Liverpool John

Moores University. For the first time, primary school teachers had authoritative materials on smoking prevention which could be included in a systematic way in the day to day teaching syllabus.

****

We continued to search for major donors and Peter Johnson, Chairman of Park Foods and past Chairman of Everton Football Club, gave us £90,000 to fund one of our nurses. Peter's father had died of lung cancer and he would give us another £90,000 to fund one of our research scientists. It has been this kind of generosity which has made it possible for us to achieve so much.

****

We realised that we needed greater diversity on the Board of Trustees and were delighted when Terry Kavanagh, lung cancer survivor, and Barbara Elliot, whose husband had died of lung cancer and who had been hugely instrumental in getting our Patient Network off the ground, both agreed to join the Board and attended their first meetings in January 2004. Lord Faulkner, a dedicated supporter and patron for several years, also joined the Board at this time.

Rod Walker had resigned the previous month after eight eventful years and Graham Morris indicated that he would be leaving the following July. Both had worked extremely hard through difficult times and those who suffer from lung cancer and their families have much for which to be grateful to them both now and in the future.

****

In January the National Cancer Research Institute published its first report and confirmed that lung cancer, while being the biggest cancer killer, received the smallest amount of cancer research money. We had been preaching this for fifteen years but still it was good to see it officially recognised at last. The next thing was to correct the situation but would the big guns seize this chance? We must wait and see.

Jesme Baird was travelling around the world now speaking at meetings and conferences, enhancing the reputation of the Foundation and spreading its messages, particularly in regard to patient advocacy and the rights of lung cancer patients to a fairer deal. She was appointed to the Public Policy Committee of the

International Association for the Study of Lung Cancer, the international body of lung cancer professionals. She would later become Chairman of this committee.

At a dinner in the Royal Lancaster Hotel in London on 12 March 2004 I had great pleasure in conferring on Sir Cliff Richard the Life Presidency of the Roy Castle Foundation, in recognition of the tremendous support which he had given us in the ten years since Roy Castle died.

Sir Cliff explained, "My connection with the charity stems from my huge respect and admiration for my friend, Roy, and I am proud to be associated with the work that continues effectively and fruitfully in his name. To be given the honour of Life Presidency of the Foundation is a privilege which I accept in memory of an exceptional talent and an inspiring and courageous role model."

****

Liverpool was now seriously getting its act together on the issue of passive smoking and a new initiative – SmokeFree Liverpool – was launched, the culmination of all the anti-smoking programmes which had taken place in the city over the last fifteen years. Naturally we were an integral part of this, with Christine Owens, our Head of Tobacco Control, seconded to it for six months to help its development with her unique skills, talents and experience.

Led by Andy Hull from Environmental Health, the SmokeFree Liverpool organisation is a consortium made up of the City Council, the Chamber of Commerce, the local PCT's, North West Trades Union Council, Heart of Liverpool and the Roy Castle Lung Cancer Foundation. Lord Faulkner of Worcester, by now a Trustee of the Foundation and a passionate anti-tobacco campaigner, would introduce the SmokeFree Liverpool Bill into the House of Lords where it would pass its first and second readings. At the time of writing the Bill has been superseded by the passing of a Bill to ban tobacco smoking in virtually all public places nationally from 2007 – a tremendous step forward, which should make a significant difference to the future health of the nation.

In between all her other activities, Christine Owens conceived and developed a national initiative to protect employees from the effects of passive smoking in their place of work. The Roy Castle National Clean Air Awards were sponsored by SmokeFree Liverpool and was the first

UK-wide scheme to reward employers, who implement effective workplace no-smoking policies, by giving them a prestigious, nationally recognised award, at the same time helping them to get their smoking policy right.

There are two levels of award: the Gold Award for completely smoke free premises and the Silver for premises that provide exterior or completely enclosed interior smoking areas. Holders must also have a coherent smoking policy and a commitment to help their staff quit smoking.

The scheme is endorsed by the National Asthma Campaign, the British Lung Foundation and the Chartered Institute of Environmental Health. Amazingly, the Department of Health declined to give their support because the criteria for the Gold Award were too strict and they could not be seen to support tougher messages than had been set out in the Government's White Paper. They asked us to water down the proposals but we rightly refused.

There are now over one thousand Award holders across the country and the number is increasing constantly, protecting employees and promoting the work of the Roy Castle Foundation.

The search was now on for a Director of Development to implement our new fundraising strategy. It took several months and a series of meetings and interviews with prospective candidates before Mike Unger found someone with the background, experience and personality whom he could confidently recommend to the Trustees.

Paul Gauntlet was appointed in November with a view to starting on 10 January 2005. Amongst other things, Paul had been Director of Communications and Fundraising at the Coalfields Regeneration Trust and Director of Fundraising and Marketing at the Samaritans. Highly intelligent and a sound strategist with proven national experience and an engaging personality, he brought a new dimension to our fundraising. His job would not be easy and he would certainly encounter all the difficulties and negative attitudes which we had continually experienced from the outset.

So, we now had in place the strongest senior management team in the history of the charity. We would need all their undoubted talents to make the most of the opportunity given to us by the agreement with the University of Liverpool and we were entering yet another new phase in the history of the charity. It was never dull.

Chapter 33

Fifteen Years

We began 2005, a year that would see the Lord Chancellor, Lord Falconer, become a passionate Patron of the Foundation, with our spirits and, more importantly, our reserves high. Income for 2004 had been over £100,000 better than budget and we were cautiously optimistic about our finances for the first time in many years.

In February, the National Institute for Clinical Excellence published their recommendations for the management of lung cancer and suggested that the NHS initiate two campaigns, a national screening programme and a symptom awareness campaign. Both were music to our ears. The report also recommended that every lung cancer patient should have access to a support nurse with special knowledge of lung cancer, recognition and approval of everything we had pioneered in this area since we appointed the first lung cancer support nurse in 1992.

I was able to refer to this in a speech I gave to mark the fifteenth anniversary of the founding of the charity on 10 April 1990. Over two hundred people filled the renovated Palm House in Liverpool's Sefton Park for a Celebration Dinner on the evening of 26 April 2005. Amid the tropical plants and trees and running streams, were friends from all over the country including Glasgow, Yorkshire, London and the Isle of Man. Trying to sum up fifteen years of hard work and achievement, I said:

This is a very special occasion and I am very pleased to see so many friends and supporters.

What this charity has achieved in the last fifteen years is truly remarkable and it can safely be said that the Roy Castle Lung Cancer Foundation is now the foremost lung cancer charity in the world, leading the way among all cancer charities on issues related to lung cancer. Thanks to the amazing efforts of so many people, including many of you here this evening, the Foundation now has a national and international profile and is setting the agenda for this most neglected of cancers, truly the Cinderella of all cancers.

Let me take you back to 1990 when we began life as the Lung Cancer Fund. Although lung cancer was the most common form of cancer with forty thousand new cases every year and with a mortality of ninety-five per cent, there was, at that time:

– *Virtually no basic scientific research being done into lung cancer anywhere in the country and not much at all in other countries.*

– *There were no lung cancer support nurses, no patient support groups and no National help line.*

– *Lung cancer came very low down in the public health agenda and in the allocation of resources within the health service*

– *Attitudes to lung cancer patients and their problems were extremely negative among doctors, administrators and politicians and even among patients themselves.*

– *There was no work being done with young children before they began smoking, to help them never to start*

– *Passive smoking was something that the majority of the population seldom ever thought about – it was not a public issue.*

I had been working since 1975 as a thoracic surgeon in the Chest Unit at Broadgreen and had become increasingly alarmed at the scale of the problem of lung cancer in the region. Liverpool had one of the highest rates in the world and in my various clinics I was seeing up to ten new cases of lung cancer every week and for only one or two of them could I offer surgery which, in the vast majority of cases, is the only realistic hope for cure. I therefore approached one of the national charities with a research plan which had been approved at the highest level by both the University and the Hospital authorities but sadly they were not interested.

I felt a strong responsibility to do something and decided to take the initiative myself. And how far we have come since that inaugural meeting on 18 April 1990 in my office at the Cardiothoracic Centre at Broadgreen. At four o'clock, on a dull and cloudy afternoon, I sat down with my secretary, Sheila Christian, and one of my patients, Eric Morris, and set out my ideas on how we would begin to fight back against lung cancer through research, patient care and smoking prevention. We had no money, no institutional backing, no patrons; we had nothing except a keen sense of responsibility and a determination to succeed. I well remember people smiling at our ambitious plans and of notices being removed from walls when we began to appeal for funds.

Within a year we had obtained charitable status and appointed a Board of Trustees. We were publicly launched by Ken Dodd and Libor Pececk on 2 May 1991. Our first aim was to raise public awareness of the seriousness of the problem of lung cancer, since this was largely unknown but, within a short space of time, we had also begun to fund a research programme in the

University of Liverpool and were providing grants to Liverpool John Moores University for programmes aimed at helping young people not to smoke. My aim was that both major Universities in the city should be working to alleviate the devastation caused by lung cancer in the communities in which they were situated.

In 1992 we appointed, in my clinic at Broadgreen, the first ever lung cancer support nurse. Now there are over three hundred in the United Kingdom and lung cancer guidelines recently produced by the National Institute for Clinical Excellence, which sets the benchmarks for standards of care in this country, included the statement that, 'All cancer units should have one or more trained lung cancer nurse specialists to see patients before and after diagnosis to provide continuing support and to facilitate communication between all professionals involved in an individuals care.' This is exactly what we set out to achieve when we appointed our first nurses and it is marvellous to see that this is now established as the gold standard for all lung cancer patients in this country.

It was in 1993 that I put my ideas together for an international lung cancer research centre here in Liverpool and it was then that we approached Roy Castle to help us. Roy said that we could use his name but that he couldn't do very much for us because he wasn't very well. I think most of us saw what he did, it was truly extraordinary and in the few months he was with us before he died he made it possible for us to realise our dreams and get the Centre built – the only one of its kind in the world. Such was his heroic contribution that we put his name on the charity and the Research Centre.

Our research programme under the direction of Professor Field has gone on to gain international recognition as a result of grants worth millions of pounds which we have given to the University of Liverpool. Major companies from across the world have come to collaborate with us and three years ago our research team was awarded a very large grant from the European Commission to manage and direct an early lung cancer detection programme in ten European countries involving twelve academic centres.

We have had workshops, conferences and visits attended by leading cancer scientists from America and many other countries and the American Cancer Society has hosted one of these meetings at the Centre. A much respected cancer scientist from Houston in Texas said, after reviewing our research programme, that if we got it wrong nobody would want to work with us but if we got it right everyone would want to work with us.

It seems that, so far, we have got it right and we are close to defining the genetic fingerprint of lung cancer in susceptible individuals. Professor Field tells me that we are eighty per cent there. Won't it be a wonderful day when we are one hundred per cent there – and it's not too distant – when we will fully understand all the genetic mistakes and abnormalities that go to make up lung cancer. We will then be able to develop tools to attack it, to treat it, to cure it and to prevent it.

Our Patient Care division has achieved wonderful things under the direction of Dr Jesme Baird. We now manage twenty-five support groups around the UK for lung cancer patients and their families, we provide a free national help line, we make available extensive information about lung cancer through literature and our website and we lobby intensively for equality of access to investigation and treatment for lung cancer patients.

Dr Baird chairs the NICE committee responsible for setting standards of care in lung cancer and both she and Terry Kavanagh sit on the recently established national body which advises the government on lung cancer issues. In November last year, in the face of competition from America and Japan, the Roy Castle Foundation was awarded the secretariat of the Global Lung Cancer Coalition, an association of lung cancer organisations around the world, of which we were founder members. How far we have come in fifteen years!

And all the while, of course, Christine Owens and our tobacco control team have worked hard to help people stop smoking and to protect them from the effects of passive smoking. Since I addressed the full Liverpool City Council in 1991, we have constantly highlighted the problem of smoking in Liverpool and our Fag Ends team have achieved smoking cessation results as good as anyone in the country and better than most.

Through grants given to John Moores University we have carried out unique and invaluable research into the attitudes to and perceptions of smoking among primary school children in Liverpool. The results of these studies have produced teaching materials which are now available to primary schools all over England which aim to prevent children ever starting to smoke.

We have a very active programme with young people through our KATS programme – Kids Against Tobacco Smoke. And, as everyone knows, since we highlighted the whole issue of passive smoking when Roy Castle was dying, the public drive to ensure healthy air for all non smokers has gained massive momentum and we are immensely proud to play an important part in the outstanding campaign by Liverpool to become a smoke free city. Many lives and much suffering will be saved by this initiative. We can safely say, in all humility, that the Roy Castle Foundation has truly become an authoritative voice on all smoking issues.

So there we have it – God has been very good and, from a standing start, we have made remarkable progress thanks to the efforts of some outstanding people and the support of many thousands more. We can be proud of what we have all achieved but we cannot rest on our laurels – there is still a lot to do and we need your help to do it.

We have in place now the best administrative team in the history of the charity with Mike Unger, Paul Gauntlett, Paula Chadwick and the rest of our Senior Management group. I have no doubt that, if you give us the means, but only if you give us the means, we will, in due course of time, achieve the mission we set ourselves fifteen years ago – to make a significant and effective contribution to the worldwide effort to prevent and defeat lung cancer.

The last fifteen years have been an amazing journey in pursuit of this mission but the next fifteen years will be crucial and it is on these that we will be judged.